DESIGN AND TECHNOLOGY

FOOD TECHNOLOGY
to
GCSE

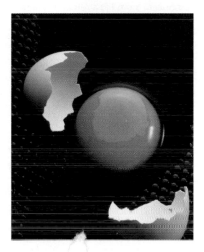

Anita Tull

OXFORD UNIVERSITY PRESS

Oxford University Press, Great Clarendon Street, Oxford OX2 6DP

Oxford   New York
Athens Auckland Bangkok Bogota
Buenos Aires Calcutta Cape Town Chennai Dar es Salaam Delhi
Florence Hong Kong Istanbul Karachi
Kuala Lumpur Madrid Melbourne
Mexico City Mumbai Nairobi Paris São Paolo Singapore
Taipei Tokyo Toronto Warsaw

and associated companies in
Berlin Ibadan

Oxford is a trademark of Oxford University Press

© Anita Tull 1998
First published 1998
Reprinted 1998

A CIP record for this book is available from the British Library.

Typeset in Frutiger and Minion

Printed in Italy

ISBN 0 19 832788 9

Introduction

This book has been written for students working towards GCSE Design and Technology: Food Technology. All GCSE syllabuses have been considered, and the book provides a comprehensive reference bank to support your coursework, investigations and revision.

A range of food related topics are introduced which will help to develop your understanding of the nature of food, and how new food products are designed, developed, manufactured and marketed.

The book is set out in double-page spreads, each starting with a clear set of objectives, and grouped in chapters in the following sequence to help you follow the GCSE course:

- ☐ The design process
- ☐ Food as a material
- ☐ The food processing stages, including primary and secondary processing
- ☐ Working with foods, including the factors that affect food and the food production processes
- ☐ Systems and control
- ☐ Product analysis and target groups
- ☐ Quality and presentation
- ☐ Health and safety

Questions are provided on each spread to test your knowledge and understanding. These are at both Foundation and Higher level. Higher level questions have numbers appearing like this **3**.

The food production industry is large, diverse and interesting, and at times controversial and exciting. It embraces many kinds of new technology, and new products are continually being developed and introduced into shops and restaurants. The book includes examples of several real-life small food businesses as well as some of the major companies which together illustrate the processes of food manufacture today.

Use the information in this book to help you create and develop your own ideas for new food products, and enjoy the course.

Anita Tull

Contents

1.1 MARKET RESEARCH

- understand how ideas for a new food product are developed
- recognize the importance of market research

Food production is a large, fast-moving business. Every week, many new food products become available in the shops, but many of these fail to make a profit, and are taken out of production. Like any new product, food must sell enough to pay for: the designing, testing, producing, promoting and advertising processes, the interest on any money borrowed for product development and any product failures that occur during the design process. Once these have been paid for, the product 'breaks even', and then starts to make a profit. It may take several years for this to happen.

There are various possible 'triggers' for the design of new food products, including:

- [ ] an enquiry or a suggestion from a customer
- [ ] what the manufacturer thinks people might want and need
- [ ] findings from research
- [ ] loss of sales to other manufacturers (competitors)
- [ ] problems with existing products (e.g. undesirable changes in flavour, colour, odour or texture before the use-by date, or damage to the product because of unsuitable packaging)
- [ ] changes in regulations and legislation
- [ ] trends, e.g. eating habits, economic factors or health issues.

Market research

Whatever triggers the design of a new product, the start of its development should be backed up by **market research**.

The purpose of market research is to **identify the market** for a product, i.e. find out which group(s) of people will buy it (see Section 6.3). Market research aims to answer a number of questions.

Surveys conducted amongst customers in shopping centres provide market researchers with data about people's shopping habits and lifestyles.

Why do people buy certain products?

There are many reasons for choosing specific products, such as:

- ☐ reliability, quality and familiarity (knowing what to expect)
- ☐ safety or meeting standards required by law
- ☐ price (depending on their income)
- ☐ availability (depending on time and shopping facilities)
- ☐ ease of use (**ergonomics**) and storage
- ☐ size or number of portions
- ☐ status, image and aesthetics (packaging and appearance)
- ☐ shelf-life
- ☐ manufacturer's reputation.

Customers are often presented with a large choice of similar products. How do manufacturers try to influence them?

What types of lifestyle do people have?

Lifestyles influence where and when people shop for food and what they buy. Lifestyles vary and may alter as a result of entering a different stage of life or marital status; a change in employment, income or leisure time; ownership of domestic appliances (freezer, refrigerator or microwave), TV or car; increased awareness of health, environmental, legal and financial issues; or changing accommodation.

What would influence consumers to buy a new product?

Consumers are influenced by a number of factors, such as peer group pressure, advertising, association of a product with a celebrity or concern about welfare of others (e.g. Traidcraft products), or political and moral issues (e.g. a company's link with a political party, or a country's involvement with a particular activity or political regime).

Collecting data

Market researchers' methods of obtaining information include:

- ☐ observation, e.g. of shopping habits, selection of meals in a canteen
- ☐ questionnaires and surveys, e.g. in a shopping precinct, through the post, door-to-door, in a magazine, a TV poll
- ☐ secondary research, e.g. using Government research data; analysing competitors' successes and failures; collecting sales information.
- ☐ testing e.g. attitudinal tests, ranking tests (see Section 6.1 and 6.2).

---

1 List five 'triggers' which can prompt the design of a new product.

2 What is market research, and why is it important to the success of a new product?

3 What methods do market researchers use to find out information?

4 List five reasons why people's lifestyles change over a number of years. Give reasons and examples with your answers.

5 Why do the following have an influence on which food products people choose to buy:
a) peer group pressure b) advertising c) political issues?
Give reasons and examples.

1.2 PRODUCT DEVELOPMENT

BY THE END OF THIS SECTION, YOU SHOULD BE ABLE TO:

- identify the various stages involved in the design and manufacture of new food products

After the need for a new product has been identified, the next stage of the process is to specify what type of product is to be developed. Designers are given the **criteria** (the standards and limits) that the product must meet. The **design specification** could include the following criteria:

- ☐ use of the product (e.g. as a snack or main meal)
- ☐ method of preparation, heating or serving
- ☐ minimum or maximum nutrient content
- ☐ expected shelf-life
- ☐ type of storage
- ☐ target group
- ☐ cost.

Research

Before ideas are put together for the new product, research is conducted to support the specification. The research investigates competitors' products, ingredients, recipes, dietary needs, food safety, methods of manufacture, suitable packaging and additives.

Generating and developing ideas

Ideas are generated by looking at existing ideas and solutions, by studying surveys and research, and by brainstorming. Brainstorming is a problem solving activity, where a group of people try to find the solution to a specific problem by putting all their ideas together, then evaluating them, and finally choosing a solution.

From a large number of ideas, only one or two may be considered good enough to be developed. Product development involves making detailed plans about many aspects including the recipe, flavour, texture, size, shape, colour, packaging and manufacturing equipment.

Making the product

The developed idea is then made into the first real product (the **prototype**). Information is collected at each stage of manufacture to enable any problems to be eliminated in the finished product (e.g. separation of a mixture when left to stand, packaging too hard to open, flavour becomes too intense, or colour fades) .

Computer models can be used to predict the effects of changing the type or amount of a particular ingredient, e.g. how it affects the shelf-life, mixing or dissolving properties of the product. Computer models are also used to give a nutritional or cost profile to enable manufacturers to decide which ingredients to use and how to price the product.

Evaluation and modification

The product is tested by trained assessors and members of the public. Their responses to and opinions about the product are collected and recorded as **data** (figures). The data is then evaluated to see if the product:

☐ fulfils the purpose for which it was designed
☐ meets the needs and wants of the target group
☐ has consumer appeal
☐ is easy to manufacture, transport and store
☐ affects the environment at any stage
☐ is economic to produce
☐ is safe.

Modifications may need to be made, and the product evaluated again.

Product trial

The finished product may be advertised and put on sale in one area of the country as a **product trial**. The results of sales and reactions to the product will be evaluated before deciding to promote it in other regions. The results of the trial might mean that the product is withdrawn at this stage because of a poor response, or the manufacturer may decide to trial the product in another region to see if that makes a difference to sales.

Consumers are encouraged to try out new or improved products and taste a sample at the promotional stands frequently seen in supermarkets and at exhibitions.

Existing products are sometimes modified or updated, e.g. a snack cheese biscuit may have more cheese flavour added, or be made with less fat or salt, and this will need to be trialled, before discontinuing the original product. It is possible that there may be considerable consumer resistance to changing a product which has been successful for a long time.

1 What is a product specification, and what might it include for a food product?

2 Why is research important when making a specification?

3 What type of research is needed when designing a new food product?

4 How are ideas for new food products developed?
Who would be involved in product development in a large food manufacturing company?

5 Once a new food product has been made, how and why is it evaluated?

6 How might a food manufacturer carry out a product trial in an area, and how would they evaluate its success?

7 What possible reasons might there be for the failure of many new food products to be successful?

2.1 CHARACTERISTICS OF FOOD

By the end of this section, you should be able to:

- identify the main characteristics of food
- understand that all foods are a mixture of these characteristics
- understand the importance of the senses in relation to the enjoyment of food

All foods are made of combinations of different chemical elements. The arrangement of molecules determines the nutrients, colours, flavours, aromas and amount of water in the food, as well as the way in which the food reacts e.g. to heat, cold or acid. These are the **characteristics** of a food. The art of cooking is to combine these characteristics in interesting, enjoyable and beneficial ways to encourage people to eat them.

Why characteristics change
Food characteristics can be affected by a number of factors.

Time
All foods gradually change over time. Some foods, such as wheat grains, remain **stable** (do not change) for many years, whereas others, such as strawberries and fish, become unfit to eat within hours if they are not preserved. Changes in food such as **ripening** and **rancidity** (when fat 'goes off') are caused by **enzymes** which are proteins produced by living cells that act as catalysts for chemical reactions. **Micro-organisms** (bacteria, moulds and yeasts) gradually make food unpalatable and unsafe to eat.

Wheat grains can remain unchanged for years but strawberries become unfit to eat after a few hours.

Temperature
Cooking causes many changes in foods, e.g. meat changes colour and becomes tender; bread dough rises, sets and develops a golden crust; eggs become solid and the clear white becomes opaque; lentils absorb water, swell and become soft.

Cooling also causes changes in foods, e.g. jellies set; cooked meat becomes more solid; melted fat becomes solid.

Freezing enables many foods to be kept for a long time but can cause undesirable changes in foods, e.g. strawberries and cucumbers go mushy when they thaw.

Other factors
The following also change the characteristics of foods:
- ☐ combining different foods (see Sections 4.2 and 4.3)
- ☐ using additives, such as colours and flavours (see Section 4.5)
- ☐ processing, such as chopping, puréeing, milling and hydrogenating (see Section 3.1)
- ☐ preserving methods, such as pickling, dehydrating and salting (see Section 3.17).

The senses

We respond to the characteristics of food with our **senses**.

Sight

The visual appearance of food strongly influences our expectations and enjoyment of it.

Smell

Humans can distinguish between 4000 and 10000 different odours. Smell receptors are found in the upper nasal cavity. The smell of food strongly influences our expectation and enjoyment of food. It triggers off salivation which helps in the breakdown of food as we eat. Taste and smell together enable us to detect and enjoy flavour. People who have lost their sense of smell have a poor sense of taste and flavour.

Touch

Sensory receptors are present in many parts of the body including the skin, muscles, tongue, roof of mouth, gums, teeth and joints. They detect pain, temperature, pressure and touch. An important factor in the enjoyment of food is texture and **mouthfeel** (the sensations felt in the mouth when a food is placed in it, e.g. chewy, slimy, greasy, juicy, crunchy).

Taste

Taste receptors are found mainly on the tongue (**taste buds**), and in the soft palate and epiglottis. Different receptors respond to four groups of taste as shown in the diagram opposite.

Freshly baked bread has a distinctive, appetizing smell.

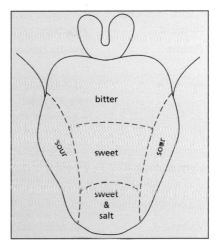
Sweet, sour, bitter and salt tastes are detected by the different taste buds in certain areas of the tongue.

1 What are the main characteristics of food?

2 Why do foods change after they are harvested or slaughtered?

3 What are the senses that help us enjoy food?

4 Why does a food such as a cucumber have a different effect on the senses compared to foods such as a curry or chocolate?

5 What changes happen to the following foods when they are cooked: meat, eggs, potatoes, cheese, cabbage?

6 Why will a wheat grain remain stable for many years, whereas fresh, untreated milk left in a warm room will become unfit to drink within hours?

7 What effect does having a heavy cold have on someone's enjoyment of food?

8 Why is it necessary or desirable to cook the following foods: chicken, potato, bread dough, dried lentils, a roux sauce?

2.2 NUTRIENTS (1)

BY THE END OF THIS SECTION, YOU SHOULD BE ABLE TO:

- understand that most foods contain more than one nutrient
- understand that some foods are rich sources and some are poor sources of the same nutrient
- understand the need for people to eat a mixture of foods to stay healthy

Nutrients are substances found in plant and animal foods. Animals and plants use nutrients for energy, growth, reproduction and staying healthy. Nutrients are therefore essential to life. **Nutrition** is the study of nutrients.

Most foods contain more than one nutrient. The **source** of a nutrient is the food in which it is found. **Rich sources** of a nutrient contain the highest amounts, e.g. blackcurrants are a rich source of vitamin C. **Important sources** of a nutrient contain less than rich sources, but because the food is eaten in large amounts, its nutritional value is significant, e.g. potatoes are an important source of vitamin C. **Poor sources** of a nutrient do not contain enough to contribute significantly to the health of a person, e.g. mushrooms are a poor source of vitamin C. **Energy-dense foods** supply the body with a high source of energy in a small amount of food. Food such as chocolate, which contains a high percentage of fat and sugar, are energy-dense.

We should eat a mixture of foods every day to obtain all the nutrients we need. If one or more nutrient is in short supply for a length of time, we suffer from a **deficiency**, and become ill. The following table shows functions and sources of nutrients.

Nutrient functions and sources			
Nutrient	**Function**	**Sources**	**Result of deficiency**
Protein	growth; healing; energy	meat, fish, eggs, milk, cheese, cereals, pulses, some nuts	poor growth; slow healing
Fat	provides and stores energy; insulates body; protects organs and skeleton; provides vitamins A, D, E, K	meat, oily fish, dairy foods, margarine, vegetable oils and fats, suet, nuts, seeds, foods cooked in fat, egg yolk	deficiency of vitamins A, D, E and K, and essential fatty acids needed for growth of body tissues, especially in young children
Carbohydrate	provides energy	bread, cereals, vegetables, fruit, sugars	lack of energy
Fat-soluble vitamins			
Vitamin A	aids night vision; keeps mucous membranes moist; keeps skin healthy; growth	retinol (animal products): dairy produce, egg yolk, oily fish, fish liver oils; beta-carotene (plant products): margarine, carrots, spinach, apricots, watercress, parsley	night blindness leading to total blindness; dry, infected skin and mucous membranes; poor growth
Vitamin D (cholecalciferol)	helps absorption of calcium; helps form strong bones and teeth	fish liver oils, liver, oily fish, milk, margarine	weak bones leading to rickets; poor growth
Vitamin E (tocopherol)	keeps cell membranes healthy; helps protect against heart disease	lettuce, peanuts, seeds, wheatgerm, vegetable oils	muscle tissue damage; swelling of fatty tissue; increased breakdown of red blood cells
Vitamin K	helps blood to clot after an injury	many foods, especially green leafy vegetables	rare – blood fails to clot properly: most likely to occur in new-born babies

Nutrient	Function	Sources	Result of deficiency
Water-soluble vitamins			
Vitamin B group			
thiamin	releases energy from carbohydrates; growth; aids nervous system	yeast, yeast extract, cereals, cereal products, meat, eggs, milk	poor concentration and memory; anxiety; weak muscles; poor growth;
riboflavin	releases energy from carbohydrates, proteins and fats; growth		beri-beri; poor growth; skin infection; eye infection; sore mouth
nicotinic acid	releases energy from carbohydrates		dermatitis; confusion; loss of memory; diarrhoea
cobalamin (B12)	helps body use protein properly; involved in many chemical reactions in body		anaemia
folic acid (folate)	release of energy from food; helps make red blood cells		poor growth; may lead to spina bifida in unborn baby; megaloblastic anaemia
Vitamin C (ascorbic acid)	helps body absorb iron; helps make strong bones and teeth, blood, blood vessels and connective tissue; keeps skin and digestive system healthy	*rich sources*: blackcurrants, oranges, lemons, grapefruit, kiwi fruit, peppers; *important sources*: potatoes, cabbage, peas, beansprouts	loose teeth; bleeding gums; weakness; loss of weight slow healing; scurvy
Minerals			
Calcium	makes strong bones and teeth; helps blood to clot; keeps muscles and nerves healthy	dairy produce, bread (added by law), cereals, leafy vegetables, canned fish bones, water from chalky areas	bones and teeth become weak; muscles and nerves don't work properly; may result in osteoporosis in old age
Iron	helps produce haemoglobin which takes oxygen around the body	liver, kidney, cocoa, curry powder, white bread (added), dried fruit, lentils, treacle, green leafy vegetables	tiredness; weakness; pale skin; anaemia
Phosphorus	same as calcium; releases energy from food	found in all plant and animal cells	not known
Chloride, potassium, sodium	keep body fluids at the right concentration	salt, salty foods, many other foods	muscle cramps may occur in a hot climate

1 Why is it important to eat a mixture of foods?

2 Why is a food such as milk more valuable to the body than sugar?

3 Find out three rich and three poor sources of vitamin C and iron.

4 Why are the following nutrients particularly important for teenagers:
a) iron b) calcium c) protein d) thiamin?

2.2 NUTRIENTS (2)

BY THE END OF THIS SECTION, YOU SHOULD BE ABLE TO:

- understand what trace elements are
- understand what other substances the body needs to function properly
- understand how our nutritional needs vary at different stages of life

Trace elements

Trace elements are minerals which are needed by the body in tiny amounts. They include fluoride which helps strengthen teeth. Fluoride is found in tea, sea water and some tap waters. Also important is iodine which makes thyroxine in the thyroid gland. Thyroxine controls the **metabolism** (the rate at which the body uses food and releases energy from food). It can be found in milk, seafood, green vegetables and water in some areas. Deficiency results in slow metabolism and goitre (swollen thyroid).

Other trace elements include copper, manganese, cobalt, nickel, zinc and chromium.

Green vegetables, milk, fish and tea are good sources of some of the vital trace elements.

Water and fibre

Water is also needed by the body, but is not strictly a nutrient. Water is vital to life. It lubricates the joints in the body and keeps membranes moist and healthy. All body fluids are mostly water.

Also important are non-starch polysaccharides (called **NSP** or **fibre**) which enable **faeces** (solid waste products) to be removed easily from the body, by making them soft and bulky. Wholegrain cereals, cereal products, fruit and vegetables are good sources of fibre. Insufficient fibre can result in constipation, leading to bowel disease.

Nutritional needs

At different stages of life, our need for particular nutrients and energy from food changes, as shown in the following graphs:

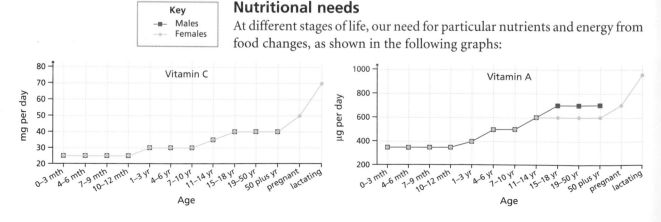

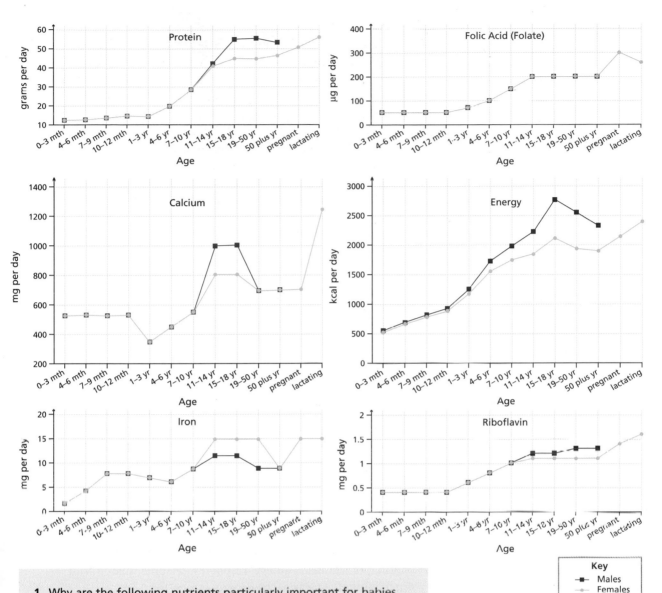

Key
■— Males
●— Females

1 Why are the following nutrients particularly important for babies and children: **a)** protein **b)** calcium **c)** vitamin D?

2 What is NSP? Name three sources of NSP.

3 Name two trace elements and their sources.

4 Why do protein requirements go up so much during late childhood and teenage years?

5 Why do pregnant females need extra folate?

6 Why does the requirement for calcium increase during the teenage years?

7 Why do female teenagers and adults require more iron than males?

8 Why do energy requirements fall in adulthood and old age?

2.3 VEGETABLES AND FRUITS

- identify which part of a plant vegetables and fruits come from
- recognize the importance of vegetables and fruits in the diet

Vegetables and fruits are edible plants which are eaten either raw or cooked. Generally fruits are eaten as a sweet food and vegetables as savoury foods, but there are exceptions. The main types of edible plant are as follows:

- **seeds and pods**: peas, beans, pulses
- **leaves**: cabbage, cress, chicory, Chinese leaves, endive, kale, kohlrabi, lettuce, spring greens, Brussels sprouts, spinach, watercress, herbs
- **stems**: celery, rhubarb
- **tubers**: cassava, eddoes, Jerusalem artichokes, potatoes, yams
- **flowers**: broccoli (calabrese), cauliflower
- **bulbs**: leeks, onions, spring onions, shallots, garlic
- **roots**: beetroot, celeriac, mooli, parsnip, radish, salsify, swede, turnip
- **fruits** (usually eaten with savoury foods): ackee, aubergine, avocado, capsicum (pepper), courgette (zucchini), cucumber, marrow, okra (ladies' fingers), squash, tomato
- **fruits** (usually eaten as a sweet food): apple, apricot, banana, blackberry, blackcurrant, cherry, clementine, damson, date, fig, gooseberry, grape, grapefruit, greengage, grenadillo, kiwi fruit, kumquat, lemon, lime, lychee, mango, melon, nashi pear, nectarine, orange, passion fruit, paw paw (papaya), peach, pear, pineapple, plum, pomegranate, quince, raspberry, satsuma, sharon fruit (persimmon), star fruit, strawberry, tangerine.

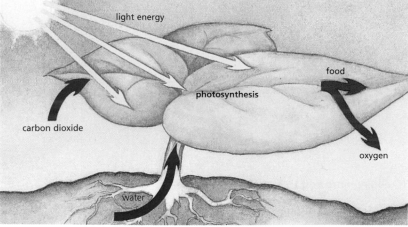

Plants make their own food by photosynthesis.

Photosynthesis

Plants make their own food by the process of **photosynthesis**, then store it for future use in various parts of the plant. Photosynthesis is the manufacture of carbohydrates from carbon dioxide and water, using energy absorbed from sunlight, by the green pigment chlorophyll. The parts of plants where carbohydrates are stored are a valuable source of nutrients and form a major part of the diet of animals and people.

Food from plants		
Part of plant	**Function**	**Food value**
Leaves	contain chlorophyll; make carbohydrate	vitamin C, folic acid, vitamin A (carotene), potassium, magnesium, water, fibre
Stems	transport water and soil minerals to leaves	water, fibre
Fruits	contain seeds; attract animals to eat them and disperse the seeds	vitamin C, carotene, sugar, starch, water, fibre
Seeds	contain material to make next generation of plants	protein, starch, fibre, iron, calcium, vitamin C, carotene, folic acid, B vitamins
Roots and tubers	main food storage parts of plant	starch, fibre, vitamin C, sugars, vitamin A (mainly in carrots)

Photosynthesis mostly takes place in the **leaves**. Lettuce and cabbage are examples of leaf foods, and they are typically rich in mineral nutrients.

The **flower** contains the male and female sex organs. These make seeds and fruits.

fruit

Roots take in water from the soil and anchor the plant. In some plants they are also food stores, for example potatoes and carrots.

The **stem** supports the flower and leaves, and may be a source of food, for example, celery.

Nutrients are stored in different parts of a plant.

Colour, flavour and texture

As well as nutrients, vegetables and fruits contribute much colour, flavour and texture to the diet.

Colour is due to various **pigments**:
- ☐ green is due to **chlorophyll**
- ☐ orange/yellow is due to **carotenoids**
- ☐ red/blue is due to **anthocyanins**.

Flavours are complex mixtures of naturally occurring chemicals, and may be very subtle (as in potatoes and melon) or very strong (as in garlic and lemon).

Texture is formed by a combination of:
- ☐ different sizes and shapes of cells in the plant
- ☐ the amount of water in the vegetable, resulting in crispness or wilting
- ☐ the amount of **cellulose** (non-starch polysaccharide) in the cell walls
- ☐ the amount of starch in the cells
- ☐ the effects of cooking.

Leafy vegetables wilt and lose their appetizing texture unless they are carefully stored and used while they are still fresh.

1 What is the main difference between fruits and vegetables? Name some exceptions to this.

2 Why are fruit and vegetables important for healthy eating?

3 Find out why it is better to eat freshly picked and raw fruits and vegetables.

4 Find out why dietary guidelines advise people to increase their consumption of fruit and vegetables.

5 How can fruits and vegetables contribute to the sensory enjoyment of food?

2.4 CEREALS

BY THE END OF THIS SECTION, YOU SHOULD BE ABLE TO:

- list the main types of cereal plants used for food
- list the nutrients found in cereal grains
- understand the importance of cereals in the diet

Cereal plants are grasses which have been cultivated over thousands of years to produce large **grains** (seeds) which are used for food.

Types of cereals		
Name	**Types**	**Uses**
Barley	2 or 6 rows of seeds	used in brewing industry to make beer and whisky; pearl barley used in cooking
Maize	large number of varieties	grown to produce oil, cornflour, maize meal, corn on the cob, popcorn, animal feed
Millet	finger millet bulrush millet	important cereal in tropical countries, e.g. Africa
Oats	autumn and spring sown varieties	contain a relatively high amount of fibre, protein and fat
Rice	more than 7,000 varieties including short grain (Carolina), long grain (patna, basmati)	staple diet in many Asian and Far Eastern countries
Wild rice		not a real rice, but the seeds of a reed-like plant which grows in Canada, China and Japan
Rye		mainly grown to produce bread, crispbreads and alcohol
Sorghum		main cereal in many parts of Africa
Wheat	winter wheat	produces flour with less than 10% protein
	spring wheat	produces flour with more than 10% protein
	durum wheat	high protein content, used for pasta

barley

maize

millet

oats

rice

wild rice

rye

sorghum

wheat

Structure of cereal seeds

All cereal seeds have the same basic structure, but vary in shape, size, colour and texture. They are rich in nutrients and are therefore the main source of food (often called the **staple food**) in most countries of the world. The nutrient content of different cereals varies slightly.

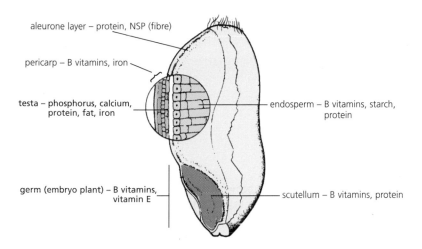

- aleurone layer – protein, NSP (fibre)
- pericarp – B vitamins, iron
- testa – phosphorus, calcium, protein, fat, iron
- endosperm – B vitamins, starch, protein
- germ (embryo plant) – B vitamins, vitamin E
- scutellum – B vitamins, protein

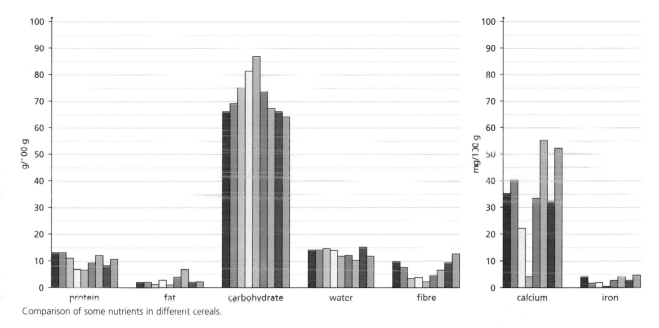

Comparison of some nutrients in different cereals.

1 List the main types of cereal plants and examples of what they are used for.

2 Why do cereals contain a good variety of nutrients?

3 Why are cereals the staple food of many countries?

4 Find out why many people object to large areas of land being used to raise animals for meat.

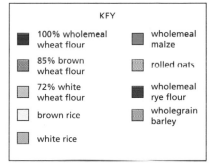

KEY
- 100% wholemeal wheat flour
- 85% brown wheat flour
- 72% white wheat flour
- brown rice
- white rice
- wholemeal maize
- rolled oats
- wholemeal rye flour
- wholegrain barley

2.5 SUGAR

BY THE END OF THIS SECTION, YOU SHOULD BE ABLE TO:

- understand how sugar can be made by plants
- understand what the word 'sugar' means
- understand the effects of sugar on the body

During photosynthesis (see Section 2.3), plants make carbohydrate and store it for future use. Sugar is the general name given to a type of carbohydrate which plants and mammals make. There are several different sugars, but all of them are made from carbon, hydrogen and oxygen.

All sugars are soluble in water. The sweetness of sugars varies. Sweetness in food has been highly prized for centuries in many parts of the world. **Sucrose** from cane and beet sugar plants is used in a wide variety of food products.

Sources of sugar			
Type of carbohydrate	**Sugars in this group**		**Found in**
	chemical name	*common name*	
Monosaccharides	fructose	fruit sugar	fruits, honey, plant juices
	glucose	glucose	ripe fruit, beetroot, onions
	galactose	milk sugar	mammals' milk
Disaccharides	sucrose	caster, granulated, brown, cube, icing, preserving or crystal sugar	sugar cane, sugar beet
	lactose	milk sugar	mammals' milk
	maltose	malt sugar	cereals

Sugar cane is grown in tropical countries. The canes are crushed to extract the juices from the fibrous stems.

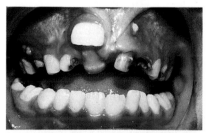

Sugar can cause tooth decay and affect the development of second teeth.

Nutritional value

Sugar supplies the body with energy. It contains no other significant nutrients. Sugar that is not used by the body for energy is converted to fat and stored under the skin. Excess consumption of sugar can lead to people becoming overweight or obese.

Sugar is converted into acid by bacteria in the mouth. The acid attacks the enamel of the teeth, and causes irreversible decay.

Honey

Honeys are superaturated solutions of sugar (about 75% sugars [glucose, fructose, and sucrose]), water (20%), and flavours (5%). Bees collect nectar (a mixture of sucrose, glucose, fructose and water) from flowers, and as it passes through the bee, enzymes convert the sugars to form honey which is deposited into honeycombs. Honey is sold as either liquid, after being processed by flash heating to 60-71°C, or solid (granulated), where the sugars have crystallized out of solution.

1 What is sugar?

2 List the different sugars. Find out the names of some food products where these are included in the ingredients list on the label.

3 Why is the consumption of too much sugar bad for the body?

4 How do plants make sugar and where do they store it?

5 There are many reduced and low sugar products available. Find out how manufacturers reduce the sugar content of their products.

2.6 OILS AND FATS

END OF THIS SECTION, YOU SHOULD BE ABLE TO:

- state the differences and similarities between oils and fats
- understand why some fats are harder or softer than others
- recognize the importance of fats and oils in the diet

Oils are liquid at normal room temperature, while cooking fats, spreads and the fat on meat are solid.

Plants and animals use oils and fats as a store of energy. Animals also use fat in the following ways:

- ☐ for protection of some internal organs (e.g. kidneys)
- ☐ as an insulating layer under the skin to preserve body warmth
- ☐ with oils as a source of fat-soluble vitamins A, D, E and K.

Oils and fats do not mix with or dissolve in water.

Differences and similarities

Generally, oils are liquid at room temperature and fats are solid at room temperature, depending on the climate of a country.

Visible oils and fats can be clearly seen in food, e.g. fat on meat, spreads and in bottled oil. **Invisible oils and fats** are present in foods, but cannot be clearly seen, e.g. chocolate, pastry, cakes, fried foods, potato snacks and mayonnaise.

Oils and fats have the same chemical structure:

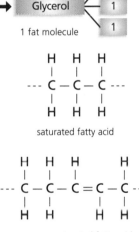

1 unit of glycerol + 3 fatty acids   1 fat molecule

The oil/fat molecule is called a **triacylglycerol** (sometimes called a triglyceride).

Most oils and fats are a mixture of saturated and unsaturated fatty acids. **Saturated fats** have higher melting points, and tend to be hard. All their fatty acids are full up (saturated) with hydrogen (H) atoms.

Mono-unsaturated fats ('mono' means one) have lower melting points, and are softer. Their fatty acids are not full up with hydrogen atoms. Two carbon (C) atoms are joined by a double bond.

Poly-unsaturated fats ('poly' means many) are often liquid. Their fatty acids have more than one double bond.

Some fats are very hard and crumbly, some are easy to spread and mix, and some are liquid depending on how much of the fat they contain is saturated, and how much is unsaturated.

saturated fatty acid

mono-unsaturated fatty acid

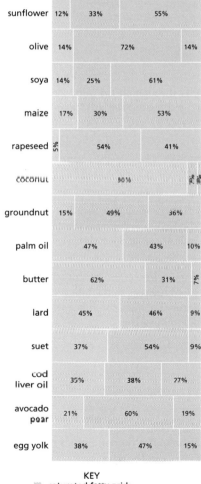

	saturated	mono-unsaturated	polyunsaturated
sunflower	12%	33%	55%
olive	14%	72%	14%
soya	14%	25%	61%
maize	17%	30%	53%
rapeseed	5%	54%	41%
coconut		90%	
groundnut	15%	49%	36%
palm oil	47%	43%	10%
butter	62%	31%	7%
lard	45%	46%	9%
suet	37%	54%	9%
cod liver oil	35%	38%	27%
avocado pear	21%	60%	19%
egg yolk	38%	47%	15%

KEY
- saturated fatty acids
- mono-unsaturated fatty acids
- polyunsaturated fatty acids

Fatty acids in different fats.

1 What is the main difference between oils and fats?

2 How are oils and fats similar to each other?

3 Name five foods which contain invisible fat.

4 Why are saturated fats usually harder than poly-unsaturated fats?

5 If someone is following a low-fat diet, why do you think it is important that they read food labels carefully?

21

2.7 MILK

BY THE END OF THIS SECTION, YOU SHOULD BE ABLE TO:

- understand how milk is produced
- understand the importance of milk to mammals
- state the nutritional value of milk

Milk is a liquid which is produced by the mammary glands of female mammals. Mammals are a group of animals which includes humans, cows, sheep, pigs, horses, goats, and many others.

The milk each mammal produces is designed to suit the needs of its baby. For example, some mammals whose babies grow very fast, e.g. cows, will produce milk with a higher protein content than milk produced by mammals with slow-growing babies, e.g. humans.

Most mammals stop drinking milk once they are weaned onto other foods. Humans continue to drink the milk of other mammals into adulthood. Human babies are often given cow's milk, but it has to be adapted to suit them by the manufacturing process.

Cow's milk has a high protein content.

Composition of milk	
Nutrient	**Notes**
Protein	
casein	80% of milk protein; in fresh milk casein is combined with calcium and phosphorus as calcium caseinate
lactalbumin	20% of milk protein
lactoglobulin	known as whey proteins
Carbohydrate	
lactose	found only in milk
Fat	found as globules throughout the milk; globules cluster together and float to the surface to make cream; contains mostly saturated fatty acids
Water-soluble vitamins	
B vitamins	some lost when milk is heat-treated and stored
vitamin C	mostly lost when milk is heat-treated
Fat-soluble vitamins (A, D, E, K)	amount depends on time of year, breed of animal, and its feed; skimmed milk contains less fat
vitamin A	carotene gives yellow colour to cream
Minerals (calcium, phosphorus, potassium, magnesium, sodium, iron)	human milk contains lower amounts of all minerals compared to cow's milk; milk is not a good source of iron. Calcium combines with casein (as calcium phosphate)
Water	milk contains approximately 88% water

1 Why do you think milk is often called a complete food?

2 Why is it better to feed human babies with human breast milk?

3 Milk is a poor source of iron. How do newborn human babies receive enough iron, until they are weaned onto solid foods?

4 Find out why and how cow's milk is adapted to suit human babies who cannot be breastfed.

2.8 Eggs

BY THE END OF THIS SECTION, YOU SHOULD BE ABLE TO:

- identify the different parts of an egg
- state the nutritional value of an egg

All birds' eggs have the same basic structure:

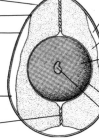

cuticle: completely covers shell

inner membrane

shell: has pores (little holes) which allow oxygen, odours and bacteria into egg, and water and CO_2 out of egg; colour varies according to breed of bird

membrane: helps prevent bacteria getting into egg

chalazae: keep yolk away from shell

thin white: becomes watery as egg ages

thick white: protects yolk; becomes watery as egg ages

yolk: membrane weakens as egg ages; colour is related to the diet of the bird; if fertilized, the chick develops from the nucleus

yolk membrane

nucleus of yolk

Nutritional value		
Part of egg	**Main nutrients**	**Notes**
Shell	97% calcium carbonate ($CaCO_3$); 3% protein	of no value, so discarded
White	88.5% water; 10.5% protein (mostly ovalbumin and ovomucin); vitamin B group	
Yolk	16.5% protein (including vitellin); 33% fat (containing more unsaturated fatty acids than saturated); 50% water; vitamins A, D, E and K; minerals including iron	cholesterol is found in the yolk fat; iron not readily available as it is bound to the protein

The main types of eggs eaten are:

hen   duck   goose   quail

1 What are the nutrients contained in different parts of an egg?

2 What are the main types of egg eaten?

3 What happens to the inside of an egg after it has been stored for some time?

4 Why is it advisable not to eat raw or only lightly cooked eggs?

5 Why are eggs not a particularly good source of calcium or iron?

2.9 MEAT AND POULTRY

BY THE END OF THIS SECTION, YOU SHOULD BE ABLE TO:

- identify what lean meat is made of and the nutrients it contains
- understand how the structure of meat influences how it is prepared and cooked
- understand the differences and similarities between meat and poultry

What is meat?

Lean meat is muscle from a dead animal. When alive, animals move about due to the action of muscles which are attached to the bones of the skeleton by tendons.

Muscles are made of cells shaped like long fibres. Muscle fibres are grouped into bundles. The bundles are wrapped in **connective tissue.** Groups of bundles are also wrapped in connective tissue, to make a whole muscle. Muscles are attached to bones by **tendons**.

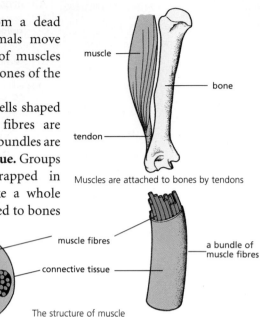

Muscles are attached to bones by tendons

The structure of muscle

Muscle fibres contain two proteins called **actin** and **myosin**. Connective tissue contains two proteins called **collagen** and **elastin**.

Invisible fat (see Section 2.6) is found between bundles of muscle fibres. Visible fat is found under the skin and is often left with meat joints for roasting to add moisture and flavour.

Texture

Tender meat has small muscle fibres and comes from younger animals. It comes from muscles that do little work, e.g. loin, rump and the top of the leg. Collagen is converted to soluble **gelatine** when heated with moisture during the cooking process. This makes the connective tissue much less tough, therefore the meat becomes tender.

Tough meat has large, long muscle fibres and comes from older animals. It comes from the muscles that do most work, e.g. shin and neck.

Flavour

The flavour of meat is determined by a combination of factors:

- the breed of animal and its diet
- the fat in and around the joint
- the formation of **extractives** (substances dissolved in water inside muscle fibres, which give meats their characteristic flavour) which are squeezed out of the meat as it cooks
- the chosen cooking method.

Nutrients

The main nutrients in meat are: protein; fat; iron; phosphorus; thiamin; riboflavin; nicotinic acid; water. The amount of each nutrient in a piece of meat will vary according to the ratio of fat to lean meat, the breed of animal and the diet the animal was reared on.

Colour

The colour of meat varies according to:

☐ the type and breed of animal (e.g. beef is red, pork is pink)

☐ the diet the animal was reared on

☐ the treatment of the animal during rearing (e.g. veal calves held in crates have very pale meat).

Meat colour and its causes		
Colour pigment	**Where found**	**Cause/Effect**
Haemoglobin (red)	in blood where it takes oxygen to muscles in living animal	some left in muscle when animal is killed
Myoglobin (purple/red)	in muscles where it holds haemoglobin in muscle	found more in well-used muscles and in older animals; meat is darker
Oxymyoglobin (bright red)	in muscle when oxygen is brought by haemoglobin	fresh cut meat turns bright red when exposed to air
Metmyoglobin (brown/red)	in fresh meat that has been stored for a few days	does not badly affect the flavour
Haemochrome (brown)	in cooked meat	formed when oxymyoglobin is heated

The colour and texture of meat indicates what animal it comes from: (top) chicken, (centre) beef, (bottom) pork

Poultry

Poultry meat comes from birds such as chickens, ducks and turkeys. It has the same structure as other types of meat, but differs in the following ways:

☐ it has less connective tissue

☐ it is generally more tender, except for leg and wing muscles

☐ it has less fat (except goose and duck)

☐ it is paler in colour

☐ it contains less iron and B vitamins.

1 What is lean meat?

2 What factors affect the tenderness of meat?

3 Why is meat from the shin of an older animal less tender than meat from the rump of a younger animal?

4 Why is fresh meat bright red?

5 Why is cooked meat brown?

6 Why is chicken better than pork for someone on a low-fat diet?

7 Why do long, slow, moist methods of cooking tenderize tough cuts of meat?

8 Why do you think the wings and legs of poultry are darker in colour than the breast meat?

9 Why do you think poultry takes less time to cook than red meat?

2.10 FISH

BY THE END OF THIS SECTION, YOU SHOULD BE ABLE TO:

- identify to which group different types of fish belong
- identify the similarities and differences between different groups of fish
- recognize the importance of fish in the diet

The flesh of fish is similar to meat, except that the muscle fibres are shaped in blocks, not bundles, and have only a thin sheet of connective tissue surrounding them. Therefore fish takes less time to cook than meat, and the flesh is more tender.

Fish take in minerals and trace elements from water. These contribute to the flavour and nutritional value of the fish. Sea fish tend to have higher levels of sodium than freshwater fish. Any fine fish bones that are eaten add calcium to the diet. Fish also take in some pollutants from water, such as metals, which is a serious problem in some fishing areas.

Research has shown that in countries, such as Japan, Spain, Portugal, and amongst the Inuit community of Greenland, where fish is a main part of the diet for most people, the number of people who are affected by heart disease is low.

Oily fish in particular contain relatively large amounts of omega-3 essential fatty acids. These have been shown to reduce the amount of fats, especially cholesterol, circulating in the blood stream. Cholesterol can become laid down in the lining of blood vessels, causing them to clog up. This makes the heart pump harder to force the blood along the vessels, and may result in heart disease. Omega-3 also makes the blood flow more easily around the body by making it less sticky.

Research into the benefits of omega-3 is continuing, and there is also evidence which suggests that these essential fatty acids may help prevent strokes and cancer, as well as help relieve the symptoms of rheumatoid arthritis and some skin disorders.

Unusual fish

Several varieties of more unusual types of fish are available in some fish shops and the fish counters of large supermarkets, including:

- bourgeois – generally a large fish with white or pink flesh which can be cut into steaks for barbecuing
- swordfish – a firm, 'meaty' flesh which is used for kebabs or barbecues
- vielle rouge – a bright red fish, with a firm flesh which is relatively free of bones
- parrot fish – brightly coloured (green, blue, and red) with a soft white flesh, which is usually steamed or fried.

Types of fish

Group name	Notes	Examples
Bony fish white fish	flesh is very low in fat; rich sources of iodine; some B vitamins in flesh; store oils in the liver which are rich in vitamin A (retinol), vitamin D, and poly-unsaturated fatty acids; good source of protein	cod, haddock, halibut, hoki, sole, plaice, whiting, skate
Fatty (oily) fish	have oil in the flesh which is darker than in white fish; particularly rich in poly-unsaturated fatty acids; more B vitamins in flesh than white fish; vitamins A and D in flesh; good source of protein; rich in iodine	eels, herring, salmon, sardines, trout, tuna, pilchards, whitebait, mackerel
Shellfish crustacea	have tough outer skeletons; muscular flesh is eaten; flesh is low in fat; high mineral content; vitamins similar to white fish; protein is rich in indispensable amino acids	crayfish, crab, shrimp, prawn, lobster, scampi
molluscs	muscular flesh is eaten; flesh is low in fat; high mineral content; low vitamin content; protein is rich in indispensable amino acids; filter feed, and will pick up harmful bacteria and pollutants from unclean water; oysters are one of the richest sources of zinc	cockle, mussel, oyster, scallop, whelk, octopus, squid

Shellfish require particularly careful cleaning and storage to ensure that they are safe to eat. Many types of shellfish are sold already cooked.

1 List the groups of fish, giving three examples of each type.

2 Why is fish quicker to cook than meat?

3 Why does white fish contain less fat than oily fish?

4 Why are many fish a rich source of minerals?

5 Why do fish such as molluscs have to be thoroughly cleaned before consumption?

6 Why is fish a useful food for: **a)** children **b)** people on low-fat diets?

7 What is the link between oily fish and the prevention of heart disease?

27

3.1 THE FOOD PROCESSING STAGES

Something which is processed goes through a series of **processes** (actions, operations) before it is ready to be used.

Food processing starts with the production of food and ends with its preparation for consumption. The majority of foods for sale have been processed. Some processes are very **labour-intensive** (can only be done by people), such as sandwich-making or making sugar flowers, whereas others require only a few people to operate the machinery which carries out the processes, many of which are computer controlled.

Primary processing is carried out on foods after slaughter or harvest, to make them ready for consumption or for use in other products.

Secondary processing turns primary processed foods into other food products, either on their own or mixed with other foods.

There are many processes used in the food industry. Some foods are only subjected to one or two processes, whereas others may be subjected to a greater number.

Potatoes are automatically washed, sorted into sizes, weighed and put into bags.

Handling materials and components

Raw materials and packaging are transported to the factory. Within the factory, materials are transported to the start of the production line. During processing, materials may be carried on conveyor belts or pumped through tubes into containers. The finished product is transported to the warehouse and the retail outlet.

Separating

The processing of the food materials might involve any of the following separation processes: **centrifuging** (spinning in a drum at high speed), e.g. in sugar production; **draining**, e.g. water from washed items such as rice, oil from seeds, blood from a meat carcase; **filtering** impurities from e.g. oil; **sieving**, e.g. removing bran when refining cereals.

Heat exchanging

Examples of processing involving cooling are chilling milk after pasteurization, refrigerating food for storage and freezing products for long-term storage. Food might be heated to destroy micro-organisms and enzymes, or as part of the cooking process as in boiling or baking.

Mixing

Examples of processing involving mixing are: **beating**, e.g. cake mixes, eggs, batters; **blending**, e.g. starch into sauces, different varieties of tea leaves or coffee beans; **emulsifying** (mixing by fine dispersion of particles) liquids to prevent them from separating, e.g. mayonnaise, ice-cream; **homogenizing** to create a uniform mixture by preventing fat droplets from joining up and floating to the surface, e.g. milk.

After bread ingredients have been mixed they are tipped into a machine that kneads the dough.

Disintegrating

The processing of some foods involves **disintegration** (making into smaller pieces) by chopping, slicing or shredding, e.g. nuts, meat, vegetables, fruit, fish.

Shaping

Foods may be formed into shapes in any of the following ways: **casting** by pouring a liquid into a mould and allowing it to cook, set or freeze, e.g. jellies, cold desserts, cakes; **extruding** by forcing a mixture through a shaped nozzle or opening, e.g. pasta, noodles, cake icings.

Coating

Food might be coated to protect it or add texture, food value, colour and flavour. This might be done by: **dipping**, e.g. meat, fish or vegetables in batter before cooking; cookies or fruit in melted chocolate; **glazing**, e.g. beaten egg or milk on pastry, sugar glaze on buns, aspic glaze on meat pâtés, arrowroot glaze on fruit flans, jam glaze on pastries.

Decoration

Decoration is intended to make a product more attractive. It might involve **embossing** by using an engraved or moulded shape, e.g. biscuits, sweets, savoury crackers.

Controlling processes

To ensure consistent and safe results, processes have to be carefully monitored and controlled. Areas in need of regulation include air humidity (moisture in the air), temperature, pressure, velocity (speed of production), weight, volume, size, machinery and stock rotation. Control may be carried out by visual inspection of results, reading data from machines or by computer (CAM – computer aided manufacture).

Packaging

The packaging process includes filling containers to required amounts, closing and sealing containers to prevent contamination, labelling, wrapping and packing in boxes or cartons.

Sliced bread is sealed into labelled packets and batched in trays for delivery.

1 Why are foods processed after they are harvested or slaughtered?

2 Why do labour-intensive processes usually cost more than those carried out by machines?

3 Find out how the following foods are usually transported to processing factories. a) milk
   b) meat
   c) flour.

4 Why do you think it is necessary to have strict hygiene regulations for the processing of meat, poultry, fish and milk products?

5 Why is it often preferable to buy ready made products such as flaky pastry, vol au vents and pasta rather than make them at home?

6 What do you think are the reasons for the increase in the number of processed foods produced and purchased?

3.2 PRIMARY PROCESSING FRUIT AND VEGETABLES

BY THE END OF THIS SECTION, YOU SHOULD BE ABLE TO:

- identify the main ways in which fruits and vegetables are processed before and after harvest
- identify the reasons for the different processes used

Before harvest

Growers use **selective breeding** to grow crops that meet consumer demands. They choose varieties of plants that have been bred to have particular characteristics, e.g. seedless oranges, stringless runner beans, high-yielding tomatoes or deep red apples.

Advances in science and technology have enabled growers to choose **genetically engineered** plant varieties. These have had a characteristic altered by changing one or more genes from the parent plants, e.g. greater resistance to disease; better flavour, colour, size, shape; longer shelf-life.

Plants are sprayed with a variety of chemicals, for example:

- ☐ **pesticides** to prevent damage by insects, small animals, slugs, snails
- ☐ **herbicides** to prevent weeds growing
- ☐ **fungicides** to prevent moulds growing
- ☐ **growth promotors** to encourage high yields of crops.

Crops are sprayed to ensure a high yield of healthy plants free from weeds and damage by pests or fungi.

Organic produce

Organic fruit and vegetables (and other produce including cereals, meat, poultry and dairy foods), are grown without the use of:

- ☐ synthetic fertilizers
- ☐ pesticides, fungicides, or herbicides
- ☐ growth regulators or stimulants
- ☐ antibiotics or intensive rearing (livestock only).

Organic farming uses traditional methods, including:

- ☐ rotation of crops to help keep the soil free of pests
- ☐ pest control using natural predators or plants, e.g. ladybirds to eat aphids (greenfly), or strong smelling plants to deter flies
- ☐ manure and compost to fertilize the soil
- ☐ growing plants with naturally occurring bacteria in their roots to fix nitrogen into the soil.

There are agreed standards for organic produce, which are regulated by organisations such as The Soil Association.

Organic fruit and vegetables usually cost more because organic farming takes longer, produces lower yields, and uses more manual labour. The produce may be smaller in size and an irregular (but natural) shape and colour, however many people believe that it tastes better, and is safer to eat. Most supermarkets sell organically produced fruit and vegetables.

An orchard of citrus fruit trees in South Africa.

After harvest

Fruit and vegetables must be processed, transported and delivered to market quickly, as many of them will deteriorate (become less appetizing and healthy) within hours or a few days.

Processing may include any of the following stages:

☐ **sorting** into different sizes, e.g. large potatoes for baking, tiny potatoes for animal feed

☐ **trimming** off excess leaves and roots

☐ **removing** misshapen or damaged produce

☐ **washing** to remove soil and stones and traces of chemical sprays

☐ **wrapping** delicate items in tissue paper or protective packaging

☐ **identifying varieties** by adding stickers and labels

☐ **storing** at a suitable temperature and atmosphere to slow down ripening.

High quality fruit is picked by hand and carefully packaged for transportation all over the world.

Potatoes are sorted and graded using a conveyor belt mechanism while people inspect them and pick out any bad or damaged ones.

1 Why is it advisable always to wash fruits and vegetables before they are eaten?

2 Why do you think organic fruits and vegetables are usually expensive?

3 How do supermarkets help consumers identify and choose certain types of fruits and vegetables, e.g. apples, pears, herbs, potatoes?

4 Find out why genetically engineered crops, e.g. soya beans and maize, have caused controversy between food manufacturers, processors, retailers and consumers.

5 Why do you think there is an increasing demand for organically grown fruit and vegetables? What are the advantages and disadvantages of crops grown in this way?

3.3 Plant oils

By the end of this section, you should be able to:

- say how oil is extracted from plants
- say why oils have to be refined

Before oil is **extracted** (taken out) from plants, the crop must be at the right stage of ripeness, free from disease and pests, recently harvested and washed. The whole process is carefully controlled.

Extracting oil

There are two methods of extracting oil: cold-pressing and crushing.

Olive oil is extracted by **cold-pressing** to make the best cold-pressed virgin olive oil. The chopped olives are pressed without heat, then allowed to settle. The oil is **clarified** (cleared) by **filtering** it (removing the oil and leaving the sediment behind).

In making oil by **crushing**, seeds or nuts are crushed in a mill to form a **meal**. The meal is then heated to release the oil. Most of the oil is separated from the meal by pressing it through a filter. Any oil left in the meal is dissolved in a solvent and drained off.

Olives being pressed to produce olive oil.

Refining oil

Oil is **refined** to remove impurities such as waxes, seed fragments, free fatty acids, colours from the seed and 'off' flavours. First, the oil is **degummed** by mixing it with hot water (80°C) in a centrifuge. The mixture is then neutralized by adding sodium hydroxide solution which changes any free fatty acids to soap which is then removed. Next, the oil is filtered through clay-based earths which absorb any colour. Impurities that affect the flavour and odour of the oil are removed by super-heated steam. This also destroys any harmful micro-organisms that may be present.

---

1 Find out why a crop of plants grown for oil must be at the right stage of ripeness before the oil is extracted.

2 Why is it important to wash the crop?

3 Why do you think some plant oils, e.g. olive oil and walnut oil, are more expensive than others?

4 Why must impurities be removed from plant oils?

3.4 ANIMAL FATS AND OILS

END OF THIS SECTION, YOU SHOULD BE ABLE TO:

- understand how fats and oils are extracted from animal products
- understand how and why extracted fats and oils are processed

There are four main types of animal fats and oils to be considered:

☐ cow's milk fat
☐ fish (marine) oils
☐ suet
☐ lard.

The breed of animal and the type of food concentrate cows are given influences the amount of fat present in their milk.

Cow's milk fat

The amount of fat in cow's milk varies depending on: the time of year, the age of the cow, the breed of cow (Friesians give 3.9% fat, Jerseys give 5.4% fat), how long ago the cow's calf was born and the feed the cow is given.

Milk fat (butterfat) is held in suspension as tiny **globules**, each surrounded by a membrane. Heat treatment such as pasteurization (see Section 3.6) damages the membranes, causing the fat globules to **coalesce** (stick together) and rise to the surface to form cream (see Section 3.13).

Fish (marine) oils

Oil is found in the liver of white fish such as cod and halibut, and in the flesh of oily fish such as herrings, mackerel, pilchards and sardines.

Fish liver oils are extracted by **rendering** (heating) the livers in water. Oil is obtained from oily fish as a by-product when fish meal is made. Fish oils have to be deodorized (smells removed). They contain a high percentage of unsaturated fatty acids, so must be partially hydrogenated (see Section 3.12) to stop them from becoming **rancid** (going off).

Processed fish oils are widely used in the manufacture of margarines and bakery fats.

Suet and lard

Suet is found around the kidneys and other organs of animals. It is sold either in solid pieces, or finely shredded by machine for easy mixing.

Lard is obtained from the **adipose tissue** (fatty tissue under the skin) of pigs. Lard tends to be 'grainy' in texture because its fatty acids form large crystals. It can be refined to make it smoother and more 'plastic' (easier to spread and work) by heating it to 105°C with a catalyst of sodium ethoxide, which alters the structure of the fatty acids.

Both types of fat are extracted by **rendering**, which melts the fat and separates it from the other materials.

Refined lard is a smooth white fat used in cooking and baking. Suet is a crumbly yellow fat which is often sold shredded. It is used for puddings, pastries and stuffings.

1 Find out why the fat content of milk tends to go up in the summer.

2 Where are lard and suet obtained from?

3 Why do you think it is necessary to deodorize fish oils which are used to make margarine?

3.5 CEREAL GRAINS

BY THE END OF THIS SECTION, YOU SHOULD BE ABLE TO:

- identify the main ways of processing cereal grains after harvest
- state the effects that processing has on the nutritional value of cereal grains

For all cereal grains, the main purpose of primary processing is to separate the outer layers of the grain from the inside by grinding or pounding. This is known as **milling**. Each type of grain is milled in a slightly different way.

All grains have to be cleaned before milling to remove debris such as dust, dirt, stones and insects.

Barley

Barley grains are passed through a rough **disc huller** which removes the outer layers. The remaining grains are passed through **pearling cones** which produce **polished pearl barley**.

Maize

Maize grains are stripped from the cobs mechanically. The grains are dampened, then softened with steam and milled, to form **maize meal** (a type of flour). The meal can be sieved to separate and remove the pericarp (husk) and the germ. The remainder is known as **grits**.

Millet

Millet seed is traditionally pounded by hand to produce flour. It is also milled commercially.

Oats

Oats are heated in a special kiln to reduce their water content and develop their flavour. The outer husks are removed by hullers. The grains (called **groats** at this stage) are sieved, the husks are blown away (**winnowing**), and any groats that still have husks attached are separated and returned to the start of the process. The groats are then cut by special rollers to produce pinhead, medium or fine **oatmeal**.

Millet is pounded by hand in this village in Cameroon, West Africa.

Rice

Rice milling is similar to that of barley. The husk is removed by pounding or hulling to produce **brown rice** which has the bran still attached. However, most rice is **polished**, cooked and eaten as white rice. The rice grains with their outer husks still attached are placed in a rice mill. The husks are removed by the abrasive action of the rice mill which polishes each grain, making it whiter. Polishing also removes the bran and germ, causing B vitamins (especially thiamin) and NSP (fibre) to be lost, and produces **white rice**. To improve its nutritional value some rice is par-boiled in water, then dried before polishing. This causes the thiamin to move to the centre of each rice grain which prevents it from being lost during polishing. Rice flour is produced by grinding and milling.

Rye

Rye is milled in a similar way to wheat to produce **high extraction rate** flour, i.e. flour containing a high percentage of the whole grain. Rye bread is dark and close grained.

Sorghum

Sorghum is traditionally pounded by hand to produce flour. It is also milled commercially. Sorghum is used for flour in many parts of Africa, and is also used in the production of beer.

Wheat

There are two methods of milling wheat: stonegrinding and roller milling.

Stonegrinding

This is the traditional method which is still used. The mill comprises two heavy circular stones with grooved surfaces which help to break up the grains of wheat. The top stone revolves on the bottom stone as the wheat is poured between the two, grinding it down to produce stoneground wholewheat flour.

Roller milling

This method is now the most commonly used means of milling wheat. A series of steel rollers, rotating at different speeds, crush the grains. The crushed grain is sieved to separate the **endosperm** (nutritious seed covering) from the **bran** (husk). The endosperm is eventually passed through more rollers to produce a fine white flour, which is finally sieved to remove wheatgerm.

In a rollermill flour is produced by crushing wheat in a series of steel rollers.

Wheatflour		
Type of flour	**Extraction rate***	**Qualities**
Wholemeal flour	100%	all of the grain is used; all the nutrients are present; high in NSP (fibre), has a nutty flavour and brown colour; has a shorter shelf-life than white flour
Wheatmeal flour	85%	15% of the grain (bran) is not used; most of the nutrients and NSP (fibre) are present; brown colour; longer shelf-life than wholemeal
White flour	70%	30% of the grain (bran, germ, fat, minerals) is not used; contains less NSP, iron, calcium, protein and vitamins; long shelf-life; good baking qualities

* The extraction rate is the percentage of the original wholegrain used to produce each type of flour.

1 What is the main aim of milling?

2 What does the extraction rate of flour mean?

3 Which main nutrients are lost when wheat is milled into white flour?

4 Make a list of the advantages and disadvantages of wholegrain (wholemeal) cereals.

5 Find out why white flour has a longer shelf-life than wholemeal flour.

3.6 TREATING MILK

- understand the reasons for heat-treating milk
- state the effects of heat-treatment on the nutritional value of milk
- understand other processing treatments and their effect on nutritional value

Milk contains water and many nutrients. It is an ideal substance for bacteria to grow and multiply in. To prevent food poisoning and improve its shelf-life, milk is heat-treated. Heat-treatment is carried out as soon as possible after the milk is collected. There are various methods of heat treatment.

Heat-treatment		
Method	**Temperature and time**	**Effects of processing**
Pasteurization	not less than 72°C for 15 secs; cooled to not more than 10°C	little effect on flavour or nutrients; must be refrigerated; short shelf-life
Ultra heat treatment (UHT)	132°C for 1 sec; rapidly cooled and packed in sealed, airtight packs	little effect on flavour or nutrients; up to 60% vitamin B12 lost after 6 months storage; unopened packs have long shelf-life at room temperature
Sterilization	113°C for 15–40 mins; cooled then bottled	35% thiamin and 90% B12 destroyed; flavour changed; long shelf-life if unopened

When milk is spun round in a centrifugal separator the cream separates out, leaving skimmed milk.

Milk is also processed in other ways.

Milk products		
Method	**Process**	**Effects of processing**
Skimming	fat (cream) floats to surface and is removed (skimmed)	lower energy value than whole milk; less fat-soluble vitamins than whole milk; average fat content is 0.1%
Semi-skimming	half the fat is removed	less energy value and fat-soluble vitamins than whole milk, but more than skimmed milk; average fat content is 1.5%
Homogenization	milk is pasteurized then forced through a fine sieve to break up fat globules; cream does not rise to surface	same nutritional value as whole or semi-skimmed milk
Drying	milk is sprayed into a hot hair chamber; dried milk powder falls to bottom	some B vitamins damaged; skimmed dried milk must not be given to babies; long shelf-life
Evaporating	whole or skimmed milk is homogenized; water is evaporated under a vacuum; sealed in cans and heated to 115°C for 20 minutes	fortified with vitamin D; about twice as concentrated as fresh milk
Condensing	whole or skimmed milk is homogenized; heated to 80°C for 15 minutes; sugar is added then heated under vacuum to remove water; cooled and sealed in cans or plastic tubes	unsuitable for feeding babies; approximately 60% sugar; over twice as concentrated as fresh milk

1 Why is milk heat-treated?

2 Find out who Louis Pasteur was. Why did he become famous?

3 Why do you think milk must be processed as soon as possible after collection?

4 Why do you think UHT milk keeps for much longer (unopened) than pasteurized milk?

5 Find out what hygiene precautions a milk processor takes and why.

6 Why do you think each batch of fresh milk is tested before it is processed?

3.7 EGG PRODUCTION

BY THE END OF THIS SECTION, YOU SHOULD BE ABLE TO:

- identify the main types of large-scale hen's egg production methods

The majority of eggs eaten in the UK are from hens. The number of eggs that a hen lays depends on its breed, age, health and the time of year. Young hens can lay up to 160 eggs a year, and this may increase to 300 a year at the most productive stage of their lives. Hens which are specially bred for battery farm production generally produce more eggs than the more traditional breeds of hen. Traditionally hens were allowed to roam freely, scratching for food. Nowadays, however, there are three main types of production: free-range, deep litter or barn-laid, and battery.

Free-range eggs

Over the last few years there has been an increase in demand for free-range eggs. Many consumers believe that free-range eggs are produced more humanely and naturally, and have a better flavour, than those produced by other methods. However, shops may charge up to twice as much for free-range eggs as for battery produced eggs.

Up to 20 000 hens may be housed in a free-range egg production unit. This may allow only an area of 1 square metre for 25 hens.

EU regulations require that free-range hens must have access to grass, but that access need be no more than a single 'pop-hole', allowing one bird at a time to go out or come in. Hens naturally make secluded nests, and like to perch above ground for security, but there is no requirement for individual nests or perches to be provided in the hen house.

The birds may be de-beaked to prevent them from harming each other when housed in large numbers.

Eggs from free-range hens cost a lot more than battery eggs.

Deep litter or barn-laid eggs

In this method, hens are housed in similar conditions to those of large-scale free-range egg production, but without access to the outside.

Battery eggs

Up to 60 000 hens are housed in highly mechanized egg production units. Hens are caged all the time with several to one cage, and are fed by conveyor belt. The eggs they lay are collected by conveyor belt. Droppings are also removed by conveyor belt and placed in a large silo for manure production. There is usually no natural daylight, and electric lighting may be timed to produce an eight-day week in order to increase egg production.

Hens are usually de-beaked to prevent them attacking each other in the confined space.

The EU does not allow the term 'battery' to be used. The eggs are labelled just 'eggs' or 'eggs from caged birds'.

Battery hens live in a confined space. Eggs are collected by conveyer belt.

1 Name three types of egg production.

2 Why are free-range eggs usually more expensive than battery produced eggs?

3 What are the arguments for and against battery egg production?

3.8 QUALITY IN EGG PRODUCTION

END OF THIS SECTION, YOU SHOULD BE ABLE TO:

- identify the effect of feed on the quality of eggs produced

Egg yolk colours are measured on a scale from 1 to 15. The yellow colour of egg yolk is due to the colouring pigments which are an ingredient of the hens' feed.

Eggs are sorted, graded and packed by machine.

True free-range hens eat a variety of plant, animal and mineral items as they scratch about in the soil. Some of the minerals are used to make the eggshell strong. Pigments such as beta-carotene from plants produce a golden coloured yolk.

In large-scale egg production, hens are given a prepared food, often called **layers' mash**. It may contain ingredients such as wheat, soya, barley, limestone flour, fish meal, vitamins and trace elements, calcium, salt, maize and alfafa.

Most consumers prefer a deep coloured egg yolk. Egg yolk colours are measured on a scale from 1 to 15 (where 1 is pale yellow and 15 is deep orange). Concentrated red and yellow colouring pigments (either natural or synthetically produced) are added to the feed by manufacturers to enable the right colour yolk to be produced. Colour cards are produced by feed companies to enable producers to achieve the desired result for their particular target consumer group.

The colour of the eggshell is influenced mainly by the breed of hen.

Collection and delivery

EU regulations do not require eggs to be collected more than once a week from production units.

At a packing station they are graded according to weight, and are checked by **candling** for any bad ones. Candling involves placing the eggs in front of a bright light which reveals any defects inside them. They are then packed. Before being put on sale, a 'best before' date is stamped on the box, and sometimes on individual eggs. The egg box will also provide information about the size of the eggs. At one time, eggs were given numbers to indicate their size, but now they are generally categorized as large, medium or small. The table below shows how eggs are graded.

It may be up to three weeks after the egg was laid before it is put on sale. EU regulations do not allow the date on which the egg was *laid* to be stamped on the boxes. They only allow the week in which the eggs were *packed* to be given.

About 10 million eggs per week are imported from other EU countries into the UK, but the country of origin is not usually given on the egg box.

Egg grades		
Size of egg	Weight/g	Old sizing
large	70	0–1
medium	60–70	2–3
small	50–60	4–5

1 Why does the colour of eggshells vary?

2 Why does the colour of the yolk vary in eggs from different birds?

3 How can consumers tell if an egg is fresh?

3.9 MEAT PRODUCTION

- identify the ways in which meat is processed before and after slaughter
- identify the reasons for the different processes used

Meat marbled with fat can be very tender and have a good flavour.

The production of good quality meat which matches consumers' requirements is a well established practice, involving farmers and animal breeders, animal nutritionists and feed manufacturers. Suitable animals are selected for breeding, and are put on a **feeding programme** to encourage the development of cuts of meat which have the required proportions of fat and lean meat. In the last few weeks before slaughter, **feed concentrates** are given to encourage fat to be laid down in the muscles. This gives a marbled appearance and tender meat.

Some animals are given **growth hormones** to increase the amount of muscle and reduce the length of time it takes for them to be ready for slaughter. There are concerns about the effect of these hormones on the long-term health of people who eat the meat.

There is also much concern about the practice of feeding concentrates containing **offal** (brain, spinal cord and other organs) to naturally vegetarian animals such as cows. Following the development of **Bovine Spongiform Encephalopathy (BSE)** in cows, and the possible link between this and a similar, fatal brain disease in humans, laws have been passed to ban these products in feed concentrates.

The treatment of animals just before slaughter has an effect on the quality of the meat they provide. When alive, the animal stores **glycogen** (a carbohydrate) in its muscles as a reserve of energy. After slaughter, the glycogen is broken down to **lactic acid**, which helps to preserve the meat.

If the animal is rested and not stressed just before slaughter there will be a store of lactic acid in the meat. If the animal has been exercised, has endured a long journey or has struggled, it will have used up the glycogen stores, and its meat will contain little lactic acid. As a result, the meat will be sticky, slimy and will not keep fresh for long.

After slaughter, the blood is allowed to drain from the carcases, and the skins and hides are removed. The carcase is split lengthways, and the internal organs are taken out. The brain and spinal cord must be removed from beef. Other offal (heart, tongue, liver, kidneys and pancreas) are put aside. Beef carcases are separated into two halves, and those of lambs, sheep, pigs and calves are kept whole.

Meat carcases must be hung (not stacked together) at a temperature of 1°C, so that the enzymes in them have time to tenderize the meat.

At all stages, high standards of hygiene must be maintained and thorough inspections must be carried out.

---

1 Why is it important that animals are not exhausted or stressed before slaughter?

2 Why are animals given feed concentrates?

3 Why has there been so much controversy about and scientific research into BSE?

4 What is the importance of glycogen in animals before they are slaughtered?

3.10 PROCESSING FISH

END OF THIS SECTION, YOU SHOULD BE ABLE TO:

- identify the reasons for the fast processing of fish
- identify the methods used to process fish

Fish is very **perishable** (it 'goes off' very quickly). There are two main reasons for this.

1 Fish struggle when caught and die from lack of oxygen, which they can only get from water – they cannot breathe air. As with meat, struggling reduces the amount of lactic acid in their muscles (see Section 3.9).

2 After they die, bacteria break down a substance in their bodies to produce **trimethylamine** which gives the 'bad fish' smell.
Fish can be kept fresh for longer if it is:

- ☐ cooled rapidly to at least -10°C within two hours of capture
- ☐ processed in hygienic conditions
- ☐ coated in a very thin film of ice to stop it drying out.

Deep-sea fishing boats (trawlers) are often equipped to cool and process fish rapidly, or are accompanied by factory ships which deal with the catches for them.

Immediately after they are taken from the sea, fish may be transferred to a factory ship, gutted and packed in ice.

Crustacea

These must be cooled quickly after capture. Some restaurants and shops store them alive, and do not prepare them until a customer orders one, thus ensuring that they are fresh.

Molluscs

Many molluscs are filter feeders, and if they are likely to have fed in polluted water, regulations may not allow them to be consumed. Some hygiene regulations require them to be rested in clean water before being sold.

1 Why do fish 'go off' quickly after being caught?

2 What are factory ships?

3 Why are fish often coated with a layer of ice after processing?

4 Why is it inadvisable to eat molluscs which have been living near to a sewer outfall pipe?

5 Why do you think many fish are gutted during processing?

3.11 PROCESSING SUGAR

By the end of this section, you should be able to:

- understand the way in which sugar is stored in sugar beet and sugar cane plants
- identify the way in which sugar is extracted and refined

Sugar cane plants grow in tropical countries, e.g. Brazil, Cuba, the West Indies and Mauritius. The sugar is stored by the plant as a juice in the tall stems (canes), which grow to 5 metres in height.

Sugar beet plants grow in temperate countries, e.g. the UK, USA, Europe, China and Russia. The sugar is stored by the plant in the bulbous root (beet).

Processing sugar cane

Sugar cane is grown in plantations and is traditionally harvested by hand with a long machete knife, but more commonly by machines. The canes are processed at a sugar mill as soon as possible after harvest to prevent attack by micro-organisms.

The canes are cleaned, chopped and shredded. The pieces are then crushed between rollers to release the dark brown sugar-rich juice, which at this stage contains impurities.

The juice is heated with **lime** (calcium hydroxide) and carbon dioxide gas in a large tank. This process produces chalk, which collects impurities. Impurities in the juice either form a scum on the surface or join up with the chalk and sink to the bottom to be removed.

The clear juice is boiled, until it forms a syrup containing sugar crystals. The syrup and crystals are separated in a **centrifuge** (spinner). The remaining brown sugar crystals are called **raw cane sugar**. The syrup (**molasses**) is used to make rum, yeast and animal feed.

The raw sugar is then **refined** to obtain pure sugar crystals.

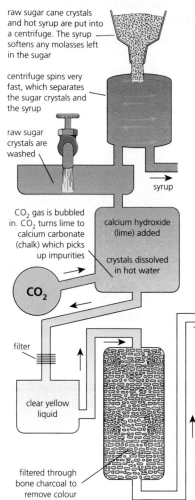

raw sugar cane crystals and hot syrup are put into a centrifuge. The syrup softens any molasses left in the sugar

centrifuge spins very fast, which separates the sugar crystals and the syrup

raw sugar crystals are washed

syrup

CO_2 gas is bubbled in. CO_2 turns lime to calcium carbonate (chalk) which picks up impurities

calcium hydroxide (lime) added

crystals dissolved in hot water

CO_2

filter

clear yellow liquid

filtered through bone charcoal to remove colour

Purifying and refining raw sugar cane

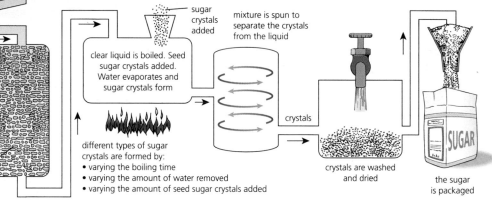

sugar crystals added

clear liquid is boiled. Seed sugar crystals added. Water evaporates and sugar crystals form

different types of sugar crystals are formed by:
- varying the boiling time
- varying the amount of water removed
- varying the amount of seed sugar crystals added

mixture is spun to separate the crystals from the liquid

crystals

crystals are washed and dried

the sugar is packaged

SUGAR

Processing sugar beet

After harvesting, the beets are stored, then taken to a sugar factory where they are washed and sliced. They are then put into a rotating cylinder with hot water, which draws the sugar out of the beet. A sugar-rich juice is formed.

Lime and carbon dioxide are added to form chalk. The chalk settles to the bottom, taking with it any impurities. The remaining pale yellow juice is boiled until a thick syrup is formed. It is left to form sugar crystals. The syrup is put in a centrifuge to separate the crystals. The crystals are washed, dried, granulated (ground into small grains) and packed.

Refining sugar

When the sugar-rich juice from either cane or beet is boiled, 'seed' sugar crystals are added. Large masses of crystals form around the seeds as the juice evaporates. Different sizes of sugar crystals are formed by varying the time of boiling and the amount of seed crystals added, producing a variety of sugars for different uses.

Sugar varieties		
Sugar type	**Used in**	**Production/Costs**
Caster fine, white crystals which dissolve rapidly	cakes, biscuits, cookies, yeast mixtures	
Granulated White crystals coarser than caster sugar	baking, sweetening drinks, sauces, desserts	most widely used and cheapest
Icing sugar fine white powder, dissolves rapidly to form a paste (icing) with water	cake decorating, icings and frostings	sugar crystals ground mechanically to a fine powder
Preserving sugar large white crystals that dissolve slowly which prevents burning when making jam	jams and preserves	
Cube sugar granulated sugar in cube form	sweetening drinks, convenient way of serving sugar in catering	made from moistened granulated sugar, pressed into a solid block and cut into cubes
Brown sugars demerara, soft brown, golden, dark brown, muscovado	baking, sweetening drinks	made either by mixing white sugar with molasses or by retaining flavour and colour of raw cane sugar by controlling the decolorizing stage
Coffee crystals large, irregular shaped crystals	sweetening coffee and other hot drinks	relatively expensive

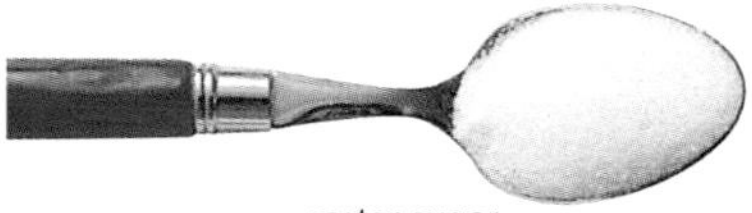

caster sugar

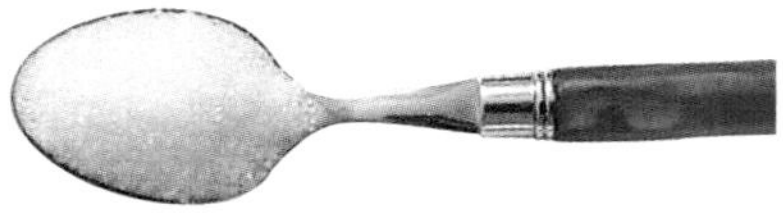

granulated sugar

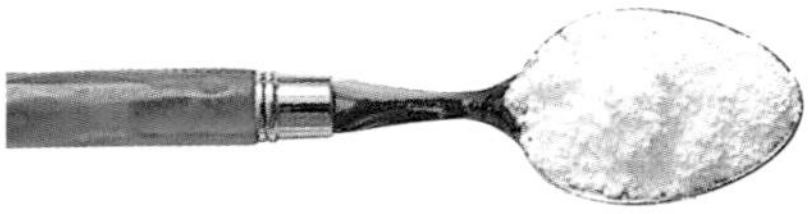

icing sugar

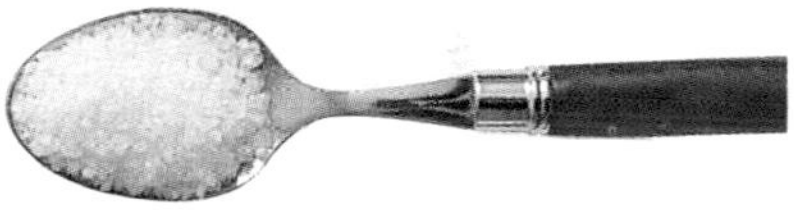

preserving sugar

cube sugar

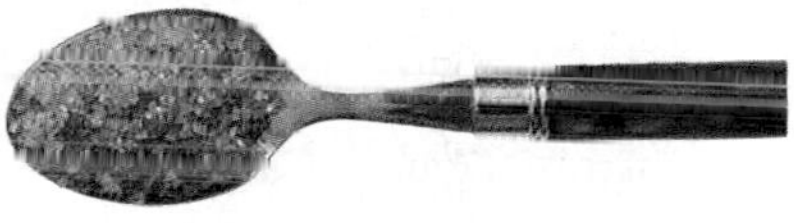

brown sugar

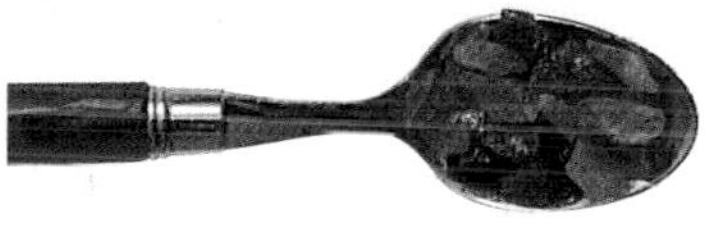

coffee crystals

1 What is the main difference between sugar cane and sugar beet?

2 What is molasses used for?

3 How are different types of sugar made?

4 Why do you think impurities have to be removed from the sugar-rich juice?

5 Find out how a centrifuge separates syrup from sugar crystals.

3.12 OIL AND FAT PRODUCTS

BY THE END OF THIS SECTION, YOU SHOULD BE ABLE TO:

- identify a number of products containing oils and fats
- understand the process of hydrogenation
- identify how hydrogenation has contributed to product development

Oils and fats (from plants and animals) are used in a wide range of food products, including:

- ☐ margarines, spreads and cooking fats
- ☐ processed cheese products
- ☐ fried snack foods
- ☐ sauces and salad dressings
- ☐ ice-creams and frozen desserts
- ☐ imitation creams
- ☐ confectionery and chocolate
- ☐ oven-baked fish, meat and potato products
- ☐ cakes, biscuits and pudding mixes.

Hydrogenation

All oils have to be **refined** to purify them before they are used in foods. After refining, many liquid oils are turned into solid fats by the process of **hydrogenation**. Unsaturated oils have one or more double bonds in their fatty acid molecules (see Section 2.6). During hydrogenation, unsaturated oil is heated and a small amount of nickel is added as a **catalyst**. (A catalyst is something which speeds up a process or chemical reaction.) As the oil is heated and stirred, hydrogen gas is introduced into it. The double bonds break open and take up the hydrogen, so that the oil becomes **saturated** and turns hard. The process can be stopped as soon as the fat reaches the right degree of hardness.

$$\cdots CH = CH_2 + H_2 \xrightarrow{\text{hydrogenation}} \cdots CH_2\ CH_3$$

$$
\begin{array}{c}
\overset{\displaystyle H}{} \quad \overset{\displaystyle H}{} \\
\cdots\ \overset{\diagdown}{C} = \overset{\diagup}{C} + H_2 \xrightarrow{\text{hydrogenation}} \cdots\ \overset{|}{C} - \overset{|}{C} - H \\
\underset{\displaystyle H}{} \qquad \underset{\displaystyle H}{}\ \underset{\displaystyle H}{}
\end{array}
$$

The double bond is lost in hydrogenation.

In this way it is possible to produce a variety of hydrogenated fats of varying hardness to suit different requirements, e.g. soft margarines (partially hydrogenated) for easy spreading and creaming, or solid vegetable fat (mostly hydrogenated) for pastry-making or frying.

Hydrogenated fats

Advantages of hydrogenation

Hydrogenation enables manufacturers to turn a variety of relatively cheap oils into similar products. It stabilizes fats by slowing down **rancidity** which makes fatty foods smell and taste bad. This increases the shelf-life of products made with them.

Disadvantage of hydrogenation

Hydrogenation causes fats to become saturated. However, an increase in saturated fat intake has been shown to be linked to an increase in the number of people with heart disease.

Reduced fat products

In response to dietary guidelines for a healthy diet there has been an increase in consumer demand for reduced fat products. The fat content of cooking fats and spreads can be reduced by adding water to the fat. Water and oil will separate when mixed together. In order to prevent separation, an **emulsifier**, e.g. lecithin, must be added, so that the water can be held in the fat.

---

1 List six processed foods that contain oils or fats.

2 Copy and complete:

It is possible to make _ _ _ _ _ fats from _ _ _ _ _ _ oils, by a process called _ _ _ _ _ _ _ _ _ _ _ _ _.
Oil is _ _ _ _ _ _ and a small amount of _ _ _ _ _ _ is added to _ _ _ _ _ up the process. The oil is stirred and _ _ _ _ _ _ _ _ gas is added. The oil takes up the hydrogen and becomes _ _ _ _ _ _ _ _ and hard.

3 What is a disadvantage of hydrogenation?

4 What are the advantages of hydrogenation to food manufacturers?

5 Find out the names of six reduced fat products and say why they have been developed and which groups of consumers the manufacturers hope will buy them.

By the end of this section, you should be able to:

- identify a variety of products made from milk
- understand how milk products are produced and the reasons for each stage of the processing

Milk is made into a variety of products including butter, cheese, cream and yoghurt. By-products from milk processing, such as whey proteins, are used in ice-cream, instant desserts and cheese spreads.

Cream

Cream is an **emulsion** of fat in water (see Section 4.1). It is separated from milk by using a type of centrifuge, which spins at about 6500 rpm, causing **skimmed milk** to be removed at the bottom and cream from the top. The centrifuge is operated for different lengths of time to produce single cream (18% fat), whipping cream (35% fat), or double cream (48% fat).

Butter

Butter is an emulsion of water in fat. It is produced by pasteurizing cream and cooling it to 10°C, then **churning** it (shaking and agitating the cream violently) for about half an hour (longer if done by hand). The fat globules stick together and form lumps, leaving buttermilk which is drained off. The butter is washed and salt may be added for flavour. Then it is 'worked' to give it a smooth texture and a maximum water content of 16 per cent.

Cheese

The process of making **cheese** from milk is basically the same for all cheeses, with variations in ingredients, temperature and time producing the differences in flavour, texture, aroma and appearance.

To make cheese, milk (pasteurized or unpasteurized) is heated to 30°C in large vats. A special bacteria culture is added, which converts lactose to lactic acid. Lactic acid acts as a preservative.

After approximately 30 minutes, the milk is reheated to 30°C and an enzyme is added to **clot** (set) the milk. The optimum (best) temperature for bacteria to grow and enzymes to work is 30°C. The enzyme is usually **rennet** (from the stomach of calves), but in vegetarian cheeses, a non-animal rennet, e.g. chymosin, is used.

After approximately 30 minutes, a solid **curd** and liquid **whey** are formed. The curd is cut and turned to release the whey which is drained off, then the curd is milled (cut up into small pieces). At this point salt may be added for flavouring.

The curd is packed into moulds and pressed, then the cheese is left to ripen, i.e. develop flavour, colour and texture. These develop as a result of the bacteria, the moulds which grow on or in the cheese, the type of milk used (e.g. cow's, goat's, sheep's) and the effects of the rennet. The ripening time varies according to the type of cheese being produced.

Cheeses are classified by texture and consistency:

- soft cheeses (no rind), e.g. cottage cheese, fromage frais, ricotta
- soft cheeses (rinded), e.g. Camembert, Brie
- semi-hard cheeses, e.g. Stilton
- hard cheeses, e.g. Cheddar, Cheshire
- very hard cheeses, e.g. Parmesan.

Blue cheeses have a special blue **Penicillium** mould injected into them, which spreads through the cheese as it ripens.

The different cheese-making processes produce cheeses with a variety of textures, flavours, aromas and colours.

Pressing curds into moulds

Yoghurt

Yoghurt is one type of fermented milk (others include cultured buttermilk and kefir). Yoghurt can be made from whole milk, semi-skimmed or skimmed milk. Any of the following may be added to vary the texture, flavour and appearance: evaporated milk, dried milk, stabilizers, thickeners, fruit (as purée, pieces or just flavouring) and sweetener (artificial or natural sugar). The mixture is homogenized to improve the texture, then pasteurized for 30 minutes at 85–95°C, to kill any micro-organisms. The mixture is cooled to 40–43°C to enable fermentation to take place.

A **culture** of two bacteria is added, (*Lactobacillus bulgaricus* and *Streptococcus thermophilus*).

The yoghurt is incubated at 37–44°C for four to six hours, during which time acid is produced, the milk proteins coagulate and the yoghurt sets. **Acetaldehyde** is produced which gives yoghurt its characteristic sharp flavour. The bacteria remain alive but inactive when the acid level reaches 0.8–1.8 per cent.

The yoghurt is cooled to 4.5°C to prevent further bacterial growth. Unless the yoghurt is pasteurized at this stage, it will contain **live** but **dormant** (inactive) bacteria.

Two types of yoghurt are made – set yoghurt and stirred yoghurt. **Set yoghurt** is flavoured then fermented and set in the pots and containers it is sold in. **Stirred yoghurt** is made in bulk, then packed into pots and containers after it has had flavourings and other ingredients added. It has a flowing consistency compared with set yoghurt.

Yoghurt is made by using a culture of bacteria to make milk ferment. Flavourings, sweeteners, fruit and colouring are added to produce different varieties.

1 Why are the following added to milk to turn it into cheese:
   a) bacteria culture
   b) enzyme (rennet or chymosin)
   c) salt?

2 List ten products made from milk.

3 Which type of yoghurt (e.g. wholemilk, thick and creamy, low-fat, virtually fat-free, natural, fruit) would be most suitable for:
   a) a 14-month-old baby
   b) a person on a weight-reducing diet?
   Give reasons for your answers.

4 Why is a centrifuge used to process milk?

5 What do you think happens if cream is overwhipped?

6 In cheese-making, why does the milk turn into solid curds and liquid whey?

7 What happens when yoghurt is incubated at 37–44°C?

3.14 CEREAL PRODUCTS

By THE END OF THIS SECTION, YOU SHOULD BE ABLE TO:

- identify a variety of products made from cereals
- understand how cereals are processed and the effects this has on their uses and characteristics

Breakfast cereals

Cereals are used to produce a large variety of breakfast foods. They are cooked in order to **gelatinize** (set) the starch they contain, providing the consumer with a convenient, ready-to-eat product.

Many breakfast cereals are coated in sugar, honey, nuts or chocolate powder once they are cooked. Some have additional bran added, and many have minerals and vitamins added to fortify them.

Puffed cereals

These are produced from rice, maize, wheat, rye and barley grains. The grains are put into a machine which has steam injected into it. This causes the pressure inside the machine to increase and cooks the grains. The pressure is then suddenly released, and the water vapour inside each grain quickly expands. As a result, the grains double their original size.

Pressurized steam can be used to make cereal grains expand to produce the 'puffed' varieties.

Flaked cereals

Flaked cereals include branflakes and cornflakes. The grains (with the shell, bran and germ removed) are broken and steamed for three hours to cook the starch. Flavourings and vitamins are added, then the cooled mixture passes through rollers under high pressure which produces flakes. The flakes are then toasted in an oven.

Pasta

A wide variety of pasta products is made and sold either dried or fresh. Pasta is a convenient food for the consumer as it requires only a short time for cooking and is very versatile.

Semolina (fine flour made from durum wheat) is used to make pasta because it only needs a little water to make a dough, so the pasta dries out more quickly. (Semolina is produced when the grain is milled.) The semolina is mixed with salt, water and sometimes egg. The mixture is kneaded and passed through rollers to make a stiff but 'plastic' dough that can be shaped

Pasta is made from durum wheat. The dough is rolled, pressed or squeezed and cut into shapes.

or moulded. Different pasta shapes are made by either pressing the dough into moulds or **extruding** it (squeezing it out) through special nozzles and cutting it to size. The pasta is dried for three or four days, or packed and sealed in trays to be sold fresh.

Bread (made from wheat flour)

Bread is made from flour mixed with water and a little yeast. This makes a stretchy dough which rises (swells up) as the yeast and sugar **ferment** (react together).

Batch baking in a modern bakery.

Flour for bread-making needs to be stored for up to two months to allow it to 'improve'. This means that the structure of the protein in the flour changes so that it will produce a stretchy, 'elastic' dough which will be able to rise when fermented with yeast. Flour improvers such as ascorbic acid (vitamin C) may be added to improve its baking qualities.

The traditional method of bread-making involves leaving the bread dough to rise at least twice, which uses a lot of time. The **Chorleywood process** was developed to speed up the process and to enable bakeries to mass produce more loaves of a consistent quality in a short time, using weaker flour. In this process the dough is mixed thoroughly for five minutes, then extra fat, water and yeast are added. Ascorbic acid is also added to alter the protein structure. Rapid and thorough kneading causes the dough structure to become elastic enough to allow it to rise in less time than in the traditional method.

Rye flour, which has a low gluten content with poor elasticity, produces densely textured bread. Rye dough often has a starter culture of micro-organisms added, which makes them acidic and gives it the characteristic flavour of rye bread.

Fast-cooking rice

This was developed to save time for the consumer and for use in ready-meals where a minimum cooking time is required. The rice grains are pre-cooked which causes the starch in them to gelatinize. They are then dried which causes the structure inside each grain to expand, so that it contains lots of small spaces. When the grains are boiled, water is rapidly absorbed into the small spaces so the rice takes less time to cook.

1 List ten products made from different cereals.

2 Why do cereals have to be cooked?

3 Find out why overcooked rice becomes sticky.

4 Find out what other ingredients can be added to pasta dough to vary it.

5 Find out why strong plain flour is used to make bread.

6 Why do you think wholegrain rice takes longer to cook than white rice?

7 Why is ascorbic acid added to bread dough during the Chorleywood process?

3.15 SUGAR PRODUCTS AND CONFECTIONERY

By THE END OF THIS SECTION, YOU SHOULD BE ABLE TO:

- understand that sugar is used in a variety of products
- understand how processing affects the properties of sugar
- understand how different processing methods are used to make different kinds of confectionery

In the UK, over two-thirds of the sugar consumed is added to manufactured food products, including soft drinks, confectionery, cakes and biscuits, jams and preserves, desserts, sauces and dressings, icings and cake decorations. Sugar (mainly sucrose) is used to:

- ☐ make foods palatable (pleasant to taste)
- ☐ make foods attractive to consumers
- ☐ preserve foods from decay
- ☐ provide texture and colour.

Sugar can be processed to control the size of the sugar crystals produced and the amount of water and sugar in a product.

Preserves

Sugar can be used to prevent the growth of micro-organisms in preserves such as jam, marmalades, lemon curd and bottled fruits.

Jam-making

Jam is made by boiling fruit with a sugar solution until it forms a gel which sets on cooling (see Section 4.1). The fruit is simmered with a measured amount of water to extract the pectin. The acid in the fruit helps with this process. Sugar is added and allowed to dissolve, then the mixture is rapidly boiled until setting point is reached. On cooling, the pectin forms a three-dimensional network (gel) with the sugar, water and fruit pulp.

Fruit can be preserved by boiling it with sugar to make jam.

Cakes and biscuits

Sugar is added to cakes and biscuits:

- ☐ to add flavour
- ☐ to help form the texture by softening the **gluten** (wheat protein) in the flour.
- ☐ to add colour by **caramelizing** (changing to a golden brown colour)
- ☐ to help trap air by **creaming** (beating) the sugar with fat so that the mixture rises when baking.

Chocolate

Approximately 70 per cent of the total confectionery market in the UK is chocolate.

To manufacture chocolate, cocoa beans are harvested then left to ferment in order to develop flavour and colour. The beans are dried and roasted, before being **kibbled** (crushed) to separate the grain and hull from the rest of the bean (called the **nibs**). The nibs are milled which releases **cocoa butter** fat from their cells.

Heat melts the fat to produce chocolate liquor (**mass**) which is cooled and allowed to solidify, before being pressed to remove about half of the cocoa butter. Cocoa butter is hard at room temperature, but melts rapidly at about 36°C (i.e. in the mouth).

Milk chocolate

To make milk chocolate, mass is mixed with milk and sugar which have been evaporated until thick. This is dried to produce **crumb**. The crumb is crushed and mixed with more cocoa butter and flavourings.

For thick, solid, moulded bars more cocoa butter is added. The mixture is then beaten and mixed thoroughly (called **conching**) to develop flavour and to improve the texture. The liquid chocolate is mixed and cooled under controlled conditions (called **tempering**) to make sure the fat sets in the correct way to form a smoothly textured chocolate with a glossy appearance.

Plain chocolate

To make plain chocolate, sugar and cocoa butter are added to the mass which is then crushed. The same processing as for milk chocolate is then followed.

Cooking chocolate

Some cooking chocolate does not contain cocoa butter, but has vegetable or animal fats added to reduce the cost and to enable it to be easily melted and set.

Chocolate is made from a mixture of cocoa butter, milk, sugar and flavourings. Thick, solid chocolate bars require more cocoa butter in the mixture than the more liquid chocolate used for coating cakes, biscuits and sweets.

Sweets

Boiled sweets

These are made by adding flavourings and colourings to highly saturated solution of sugar (two parts sugar to one part water) which will crystallize when cooled and mixed.

Fudges and soft sweets

Invert sugar can be added to sugar solution to help very small crystals to form when making smooth, soft products like fudge. Invert sugar is sucrose which contains equal amounts of glucose and fructose and is found naturally in honey. It can be produced commercially by **hydrolising** sucrose (splitting up the molecules using water). Gums and chewy sweets are made from sugar which is not crystallized, and has up to 15 per cent water in it. The higher the water content, the softer the product. Marshmallows are made by whisking air into a soft sugar mixture.

Caramels and toffees

When heated, sugar (dry or in water) will gradually change from white, to clear, to golden, then dark brown, as the heat changes its structure. This is called **caramelization**. Overheating produces a bitter taste.

1 List the groups of products which have sugar added.

2 How does sugar act as a preservative in products such as jams?

3 Why are cooking chocolate products different from confectionery chocolate?

4 What is invert sugar?

5 What are the changes that happen to sugar in the manufacture of:
a) boiled sweets b) toffees?

3.16 MEAT PRODUCTS

BY THE END OF THIS SECTION, YOU SHOULD BE ABLE TO:

- identify a number of meat products
- understand how meat products are produced

A large number of meat products are available to the consumer, including sausages (uncooked or ready to eat), cold cooked meats (often canned), pies, burgers, pâtés, cured meats and ready meals. A similar range of poultry products is available.

Meat is classified as a **high-risk food**, i.e. it is easily contaminated by micro-organisms, so the production of meat products has to be carefully controlled and inspected to prevent food poisoning.

Sausages

Many butchers make their own sausages.

To manufacture uncooked sausages, which will need to be cooked thoroughly by the consumer, the meat and fat are chopped or minced. This exposes a large surface area to micro-organisms, so chemical preservatives, e.g. sodium metabisulphite (E223), are added to slow down microbial growth. Spices, colouring and a starch binder (usually rusk) are mixed in. The mixture is forced through a nozzle into sausage skins (made from the small intestines of sheep or from man-made collagen). They are cooled, twisted into chains and packed.

Sausages such as salami and kabanos which are ready to eat, will have been prepared through a fermentation process. To prepare this kind of sausage, the raw meat is chopped and mixed with a starter culture of a special bacteria. The bacteria ferment the meat by producing lactic acid. The product may be smoked and air-dried, giving it a long shelf-life. Flavours such as garlic, spices and peppercorns may be added. Red wine is often used to add colour to the sausage. The combination of lactic acid, smoking, drying and salt prevents any further microbial growth, which means that such products are safe to eat uncooked. Some sausages develop a fine white mould on their skins which is edible.

Cured meats

Many years ago, meat was salted to preserve it. The process of **curing** was developed and has mostly replaced salting. Examples of cured meats include ham and bacon.

The meat carcases (usually pig) are de-haired, cleaned and split lengthways into sides which are cooled to 5°C and have **brine** pumped through them. (Brine is a solution of up to 30 per cent salt and four per cent potassium nitrate in water.) The sides of meat are then put into tanks and covered in brine for five days. Special bacteria are added to convert the potassium nitrate into potassium nitrite. This breaks down and combines with **myoglobin** (colouring pigment in the meat) to make the meat pink.

Many varieties of cured meats are available at delicatessen counters. The different curing processes add distinctive colour and flavour to the meat, as well as preserving it.

The meat is removed and matured to develop flavour and may then be smoked to give it more flavour. Smoking also helps preserve the meat. Some processors slice bacon and pass it through a brine solution for a short time (e.g. 15 minutes) then allow it to mature for a few hours afterwards.

Pies and pasties

These usually contain a mixture of cooked lean meat, fat, flavourings (e.g. herbs and spices), vegetables or other starchy fillers, and sometimes a **stock** (a well-flavoured liquid made from meat, poultry or vegetables by simmering them in water to extract flavour). The pie contents are set with gelatine, or a thickened sauce flavoured with, for example, cheese or herbs.

Large meat pies require hand finishing.

Burgers

Burgers are made from a finely chopped and shaped mixture of meat or poultry (e.g. beef, lamb, pork, turkey), cereal, fat and flavourings. Three types of burger are described and regulated by law:

- [ ] **burgers** must be made from at least 80 per cent meat, usually beef, 65 per cent of which must be lean
- [ ] **hamburgers** may be made from beef, pork or a mixture of both, and must be at least 80 per cent meat, 65 per cent of which is lean
- [ ] **economy burgers** may be made from 60 per cent meat, 65 per cent of which must be lean.

Pâtés

These are a mixture of chopped or finely minced meats or offal (e.g. liver, kidney), binding ingredients which might include egg or cereal, and flavourings such as spices, herbs, wine or garlic. The mixture is packed into a mould or dish and baked. Pâtés are usually eaten cold, and sold straight from the dish at a delicatessen counter, in vacuum-sealed packs or in sausage form. The meat content varies according to the quality and price of the product.

1 List six types of meat product.

2 Why is meat a high-risk food?

3 Why is E223 added to sausages?

4 Why does salami keep for much longer than uncooked pork sausages?

5 Why are bacon and ham pink?

6 Find out why cooked meats must not be prepared near or with the same equipment as raw meats.

7 Why do you think minced and finely chopped meat are more of a health risk than uncut meat?

3.17 PROCESSING FISH

BY THE END OF THIS SECTION, YOU SHOULD BE ABLE TO:

- identify the main ways of processing fish
- identify a variety of fish products

Fish is eaten worldwide, and over many years a variety of processing methods have resulted in many different fish products being available, e.g. fish fingers, oven-bake coated fish; boil-in-the-bag fish in sauce; frozen fillets, chunks and whole fish; seafood pies; and fish cakes.

Dwindling numbers of fish, the high-risk nature of fishing, and the labour involved in preparing fish for sale have all resulted in increasing prices of fresh fish and fish products.

Preserving fish

Methods of processing are usually aimed at preserving the fish.

Drying

Sun-drying is the traditional method of drying, but it is rather difficult to control. Modern drying methods include tunnel-drying in a factory or freeze-drying where the fish is frozen, and the water it contains removed rapidly as water vapour. Cod and other types of white fish are dried.

Smoking

Wood-smoked fish has a characteristic flavour. Hot-smoked fish (e.g. mackerel and trout) is cooked and dried during the process, whereas cold-smoked fish (e.g. kippers, haddock and salmon) is not cooked and so has a shorter shelf-life.

In Scotland, there is a long tradition of producing smoked fish.

Salting

Salting is carried out by using brine or dry salt on fish such as herrings. Kippers, bloaters and finnan haddock are all salted before smoking.

Pickling

Herrings can be **filleted** (have the bones removed), then rolled, skewered and picked in vinegar. These are known as roll-mop herrings.

Canning

Oily fish, such as tuna or pilchards, are usually canned, but must be cleaned and prepared first. They may be salted or smoked before canning, and are usually packed tightly in oil, tomato sauce, brine or water. Heat sterilization of the sealed cans destroys harmful micro-organisms.

Frozen fish products

Fish fingers can be made from minced white fish, pressed into shape and coated with batter or breadcrumbs, or they can be cut into shape from white fish fillets and then coated.

Coated fish portions are usually **filleted** (bones removed), with or without the skin, then coated in batter or breadcrumbs. Fish cakes are usually made from minced white fish, with ingredients such as potato, herbs and egg added before shaping and coating.

Large quantities of salmon are preserved by canning. The fish are sliced into steaks, packed into cans with oil or brine, sealed and then heated to cook and sterilize the contents.

1 List six different fish products.

2 What are the environmental concerns about the amount of fish eaten by humans?

3 What are the factors that influence the cost of fish?

3.18 PROCESSING EGGS

Large numbers of eggs are used in food manufacture for the following purposes:
- trapping air in cakes, mousses, soufflés, meringues
- thickening mixtures such as custards and sauces
- emulsifying oil and water in products such as cake mixtures and mayonnaise (see Section 4.1)
- binding ingredients together for products such as rissoles, burgers, fish or potato cakes
- coating products such as fish pieces with breadcrumbs or in batters
- glazing baked products such as bread and pastry
- enriching products such as pasta, where they are added to the dough as either liquid or dried egg.

Eggs can be dried, frozen or pasteurized.

Dried egg

Whole eggs or egg whites can be spray-dried at a temperature of approximately 71°C to form a fine powder (see Section 4.10). In the process, harmful bacteria such as salmonella are destroyed. Dried egg white is used by cake decorators for the production of royal icing. Whole dried egg is used mainly by bakers and confectioners.

Dried egg white is used by caterers to make royal icing for decorating large cakes. Harmful bacteria are destroyed by the drying process

Frozen whole egg

Frozen egg is used mainly by bakers and confectioners. The egg is beaten to form a uniform mixture. The mixture is strained, pasteurized for 60 seconds at 63°C, then poured into sterilized containers (usually cans) and quick frozen. Egg whites and yolks are also frozen separately.

Some desserts, such as cheesecake, may contain uncooked egg. Manufacturers use pasteurized egg to ensure there is no risk of food poisoning.

Pasteurized egg

Pasteurized egg can be used in products such as cheesecakes, mousses, soufflés and mayonnaise to reduce the risk of food poisoning. Whole eggs, whites or yolks are beaten to a uniform mixture, strained and heated for 60 seconds at 63°C.

1 Why do you think dried egg white is often used by cake decorators instead of fresh egg white?

2 Find out and list a variety of food products that use dried whole or separated egg.

3 Why can't whole, fresh eggs be successfully frozen in their shells?

3.19 PROCESSING FRUIT AND VEGETABLES

BY THE END OF THIS SECTION, YOU SHOULD BE ABLE TO:

■ understand why fruit and vegetables have to be processed soon after harvest

■ understand the methods used to process and preserve vegetables and fruit

Fruit decays quickly if dropped and bruised.

Fruit and vegetables continue to live after they are harvested – they continue to **respire** (use oxygen to release stored energy), ripen and lose water.

Preservation

The time taken to become ripe and then decay varies according to the type of fruit or vegetable e.g. potatoes decay slowly, strawberries rapidly.

Slowing the decay process

The ripening and decay process can be slowed down in many cases by the following methods.

☐ **Controlling temperature** Cool temperatures slow down the decay process, but are not suitable for use with many tropical fruits such as bananas, as their colour and flavour can become spoiled.

☐ **Controlled atmosphere storage** Increasing the carbon dioxide level in a storeroom will slow down respiration, but it has to be carefully controlled. If the level is too high, anaerobic respiration (without oxygen) will occur, leading to a build-up of toxic substances.

☐ **Wax-coating** The aim is to slow down ripening by preventing all the carbon dioxide leaving the fruit or vegetable while allowing some oxygen in. Loss of water can also be controlled in this way. This method is used for some tropical fruits and for citrus fruits.

☐ **Irradiation** Irradiation is a method of preserving food by exposing it to gamma rays or X-rays to slow down sprouting in potatoes and ripening of some fruits, as well as killing moulds, insects and bacteria.

☐ **Drying** Many fruits and vegetables are dried, either by the traditional sun-drying method or by tunnel-drying in hot air. Freeze-dried fruit and vegetables are of a very high quality but are expensive to process.

☐ **Preserving in sugar** Many fruits are made into sugar preserves such as jam (see Section 3.15). Candied and crystallized fruits are made by immersing sliced fruit in a strong sugar solution to dry it out by osmosis (see Section 4.13).

☐ **Preserving in acid** Vegetables and some fruits can be pickled in vinegar to prevent the growth of micro-organisms.

Candied peel is an ingredient used in cakes and puddings. It is made by soaking the peel of citrus fruits in a strong sugar solution.

☐ **Freezing** Many fruits and vegetables can be deep-frozen and will remain in good condition for months. The nutrient content, especially the ascorbic acid (vitamin C) is often well retained as products such as garden peas are frozen very shortly after harvest. Before freezing, some vegetables are **blanched** (immersed in boiling water) to destroy enzymes which can cause browning.

Canning

Many fruits and vegetables are canned in fruit juice, sugar syrup, water, brine or a sauce. Sometimes citric acid is added to stabilize the acidity.

The cans are filled with the product, carefully sealed (to prevent the entry of bacteria), then placed in a retort (like a large pressure cooker), and the temperature is raised to 121°C. The cans are held at the cooking temperature for the required time (depending on the product), partially cooled by spraying them with cold water, then passed along a bath of chlorinated water (free from harmful bacteria) to complete the cooling.

Acidic fruit and vegetables, e.g. grapefruit segments, tomatoes and rhubarb, are preserved in plastic-lined cans to prevent **corrosion** (reaction of the acid with the metal).

Canned fruit and vegetables are used extensively as a component in catering. They are a cheap and convenient alternative to fresh produce.

Processing

Peeling

Many fruits and vegetables are peeled before they are eaten. It is uneconomic in large-scale processing factories to peel by hand, so a variety of methods are used, including:

- ☐ scalding with boiling water to loosen peel and remove it by brushing, e.g. tomatoes
- ☐ disintegrating peel by using a caustic soda solution, e.g. plums and apricots
- ☐ spraying the peel with liquid nitrogen to freeze it, then removing it when thawed, e.g. citrus fruits
- ☐ using acid solutions to remove the peel and destroy the enzymes that make the fruit go brown, e.g. apples and pears.

Extracting juice

Fruits or vegetables are first finely chopped, crushed or mashed to form a pulp. Some fruits, e.g. citrus fruits, may be peeled first. The pulp is then pressed and the juices may be filtered to remove solid particles, e.g. seeds and skins. Sometimes enzymes are added to clear the juice, which is then pasteurized (see Section 3.6) before being sealed in a carton, bottle or can.

1 Find out and describe what happens to the appearance, flavour and texture of the following after they are harvested: bananas, carrots, potatoes, strawberries.

2 Why can't some fruits and vegetables, e.g. lettuce, cucumber and bananas, be successfully preserved in a deep freezer?

3 How can ripening be slowed down after harvest?

4 How does storing fruits and vegetables in an atmosphere of carbon dioxide gas slow down ripening?

5 How does drying and preserving in sugar stop fruit from decaying?

3.20 THE NUTRITIONAL EFFECTS OF PROCESSING

BY THE END OF THIS SECTION, YOU SHOULD BE ABLE TO:

- identify the main ways in which nutrients are lost during processing
- identify ways in which nutrient losses can be minimized
- identify ways in which food manufacturers replace lost nutrients

Many methods of processing foods result in a loss of nutrients, for example:

- ☐ wastage caused by peeling and trimming food
- ☐ refining, e.g. wheat, rice (see Section 3.5)
- ☐ heat treatment, either for preservation or cooking
- ☐ washing and polishing, e.g. rice grains
- ☐ exposure to air, e.g. chopping vegetables and fruit (see Section 4.11).

Protein

Protein is **denatured** (changed) when heated. Normal cooking temperatures do not affect the food value of protein, but overheating and prolonged cooking may make the protein less easy to digest.

If protein and carbohydrate are heated together, e.g. for making toasted breakfast cereals, the food value of the protein may be reduced, especially if the temperature is high.

Vitamins

Vitamins are affected by a variety of processes. For example, they may be dissolved and lost in water, or destroyed by heat. They may also become unstable and of little value to the body. For example, adding bicarbonate of soda to cooking vegetables retains their green colour but oxidizes any vitamin C, and exposing foods to light during processing or storing can destroy riboflavin, one of the vitamin B group.

Vegetables lose their appetizing colour if they are stored in the wrong conditions or overcooked.

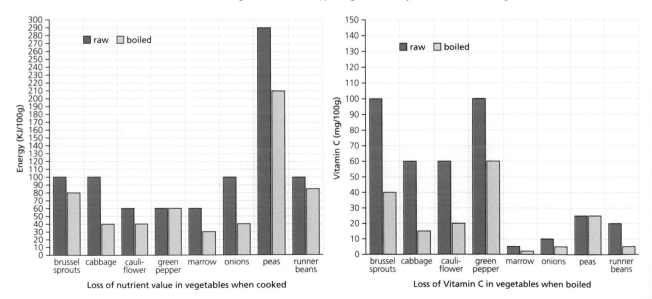

Loss of nutrient value in vegetables when cooked

Loss of Vitamin C in vegetables when boiled

Minimizing nutrient loss

Losses of nutrients can be kept to a minimum by:

- chopping and preparing foods only a short time before preserving, cooking or serving them
- storing foods in a suitable way, e.g. in a cool place, in a low oxygen atmosphere, in acid, e.g. vinegar, or away from light
- cooking foods for the minimum time required, at a carefully controlled temperature, then preserving or serving them as soon as possible
- blanching foods to be frozen, e.g. peas, to stop enzyme action destroying vitamins.

Replacing nutrients

To increase the nutritional value of a product, and enable this information to be used to promote it, food manufacturers may add nutrients to food. This is called **fortification**.

Nutrients are added to some breakfast cereals, for example, to replace those lost when the cereal grains were refined. More may be added to give a healthy image to the product. Some products, e.g. bread and margarine, have to be fortified by law in order to increase their nutrient content.

Modifying nutrients

Food manufacturers are aware of current health issues and eating trends through the work of market researchers. As a result of research, manufacturers may decide to modify the nutrient content of a product, e.g. by reducing the fat or increasing the iron content.

Many breakfast cereals are fortified with additional nutrients.

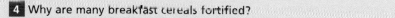

1 Name four ways in which nutrients are lost during processing.

2 How is vitamin C lost from foods such as cabbage and broccoli, and how can such losses be prevented?

3 How does blanching help to preserve vitamins?

4 Why are many breakfast cereals fortified?

5 How have dietary guidelines influenced food manufacturers in modifying the nutrient content of their products?

6 Find out what were the original reasons for fortifying bread and margarine by law.

4.1 THE WORKING PROPERTIES OF FOODS

By the end of this section, you should be able to:

- understand the properties of ingredients
- identify how and when these properties are used in the design and creation of a food product

The texture, shape, colour and flavour of individual foods result from: the **working properties** (what they will do) of the different ingredients in the food; the **combination** (mixture) of different types and amounts of ingredients used; the method of preparation, processing and cooking used.

Aeration

Some foods, e.g. sponge cakes, mousses, meringues, and ice-cream, have a light, airy texture which is brought about by the ability of the ingredients to trap and hold air in the form of tiny bubbles. Air can be introduced into foods in several ways.

Methods of aeration			
Method	**Ingredients**	**Process**	**Uses**
Creaming: beating with wooden spoon or in a food processor	fat (butter, margarine) and sugar	tiny air bubbles are trapped by fat and sugar crystals. The bubbles expand when mixture is cooked, causing it to rise.	cakes, puddings, biscuits
Whisking: mixing ingredients at high speed with an electric or hand-held whisk	eggs and sugar, egg white cream or evaporated milk	protein in egg white stretches and traps tiny air bubbles. air bubbles are trapped as fat globules form small clusters (coalesce), and stiffen the cream.	sponge cake, Swiss roll, meringue, whipping or double cream, milk jellies, mousses
Trapping: rolling and folding pastry	pastry dough	as pastry dough is rolled and folded, air becomes trapped between the layers. It expands when heated producing a light, crisp, layered result.	filo, strudel, Danish, flaky and puff pastry

Commercially produced items such as ice-cream and instant puddings rely on aeration to give them volume and texture (known as **bubble technology**). The air is trapped by whisking and is held in place by added stabilizers (see Section 4.5). Aerosol 'whipped' cream has an inert (non reactive) gas pumped into it to give the cream a light, airy texture.

The creamy cheese sauce topping on lasagne will become rubbery if overbaked.

Coagulation

The texture of foods that contain protein can be altered by heat. The structure of protein is permanently altered when heated. This is called **denaturation** and leads to **coagulation**, which is when the protein 'sets'.

Heating food	
Food	**Effect of heat**
Meat	meat proteins (collagen and elastin) contract as they coagulate, so meat shrinks; overheating makes meat hard and indigestible; heating in a liquid changes collagen to gelatine
Eggs	egg white protein (ovalbumin) becomes solid and opaque white as it coagulates; egg yolk protein becomes solid and eventually dry as it coagulates
Wheat	wheat protein (gluten) sets to form an open structure, as in bread, cakes and other products
Milk	milk proteins (lactalbumin) and lactoglobulin coagulate to form a 'skin'
Cheese	protein becomes rubbery then crisp

Emulsification

Oil and water will not stay mixed together without the addition of an **emulsifier**. The diagram shows how emulsification works.

Foods such as soya and egg yolk contain natural emulsifiers, called **lecithins**. These are added commercially to foods such as margarine, mayonnaise, chocolate, ice-cream, bread and cakes. Commercially added lecithin (E322) is mostly obtained from soya beans.

In domestic kitchens egg yolk is added to cake mixtures and mayonnaise to prevent separation of fat and oil from the mixtures.

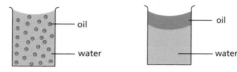

An oil in water emulsion separates after a time.

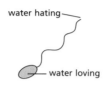

Emulsifier molecules have a water-loving (hydrophilic) head and a water-hating (hydrophobic) tail.

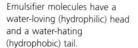

The water-loving head is attracted to the water and the water-hating tail to the oil droplets.

So the emulsifier molecules surround the oil droplets and prevent them from separating out from the water.

Setting

Certain foods are not ready to be eaten until they have **set**, i.e. changed from a liquid or semi-liquid state to a solid or semi-solid state, e.g. jelly, mousse, soufflé, cakes, bread, egg custard, cold cornflour custard, toffee, jam. There are various ways in which food sets, such as **gelation**. **Gelatine** (a protein extracted from bones, skin and tendons of cattle and pigs) traps and immobilizes water added to it in a three-dimensional protein network called a **gel**. When heated, the gel changes to a liquid **sol**. When cooled the sol sets e.g. in jellies, cold soufflés, mousses and aspic. Gelatine is also added to some yoghurts, ice-cream, pâté, canned cold meats and soup.

Jam making is another example of gelation. Fruit boiled with a sugar solution will form a gel which causes the jam to set. Pectin (a complex carbohydrate found in fruits), acid and sugar are required to make the gel. At about pH 3.5 pectin makes a three-dimensional network, trapping the water, fruit and sugar.

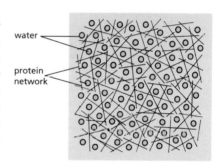

The protein molecules in gelatine trap the water and set the mixture to form a semi-solid gel.

Gelatinization of starch

Starch granules absorb water and swell when heated above 60°C. At 85°C starch granules are approximately five times their original size, which thickens the mixture. On further heating some granules rupture, releasing starch, which traps liquid to form a gel that sets when cool e.g. in cornflour or arrowroot sauces, and blancmange.

1 Give two examples of working properties of foods and how these are used in the production of food.

2 What causes a cake mixture to set when it is baked?

3 What causes a roux sauce to thicken when heated?

4 Why is bubble technology important to manufacturers of products such as ice-cream and instant desserts?

BY THE END OF THIS SECTION, YOU SHOULD BE ABLE TO:

- identify the reasons for combining foods and varying ingredients in the context of catering (domestic and commercial)
- understand the nutritional, aesthetic and economic effects of these practices

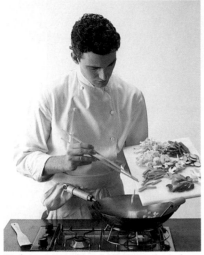

Stir frying is a traditional Chinese method of cooking. It requires only a very small amount of oil and the mixture of ingredients is cooked lightly and quickly, making this a healthy and nutritious way of cooking.

Concentrated bouillon, or stock, contains a mixture of flavourings and is widely used in catering.

The art of food production is to combine foods and vary ingredients and cooking methods to produce interesting, appetizing, economical and nutritional meals.

Traditional recipes were developed using locally available ingredients and equipment, but travel abroad has inspired people to try new ingredients and recipes. As a result of technological advances in transportation and storage methods there is now a large variety of ingredients available to people and many different ways of combining them.

Added value

In a catering context, the term 'added value' may mean adding one or more ingredients to raise the nutritional value of a product, or combining two or more sources of a nutrient such as protein, to **complement** each other (make each other of equal value to the body). Examples of this might include dipping a vegetable and nut rissole into beaten egg and breadcrumbs before cooking, adding haricot or kidney beans to a bolognese sauce or adding pasta or cereal grains to a vegetable soup.

Reducing fat

The amount of fat in dishes can be reduced by using less fat when frying or in the recipe, low-fat products such as yoghurt instead of cream, skimmed milk instead of whole milk or chicken instead of pork. Grilling or baking food instead of frying will also reduce the amount of fat in a meal.

Reducing sugar

The sugar content in many sweet recipes can be reduced by using naturally sweet ingredients (e.g. fruit or honey) instead of sugar or by using artificial sweeteners.

Enhancing flavour

Ingredients used to add flavour to food, include herbs, spices, stock, seasonings, citrus fruit zest and oils. Extractives from roast meat give flavour to gravy.

Quality and safety

Whatever combination or variation is chosen, caterers should consider:

- ☐ does the addition of a flavour, e.g. chilli, mask the other ingredients?
- ☐ does the reduction of an ingredient, e.g. sugar, affect the cooking time and finished appearance of the food?
- ☐ does the reduction of an ingredient affect the safety of a food? (e.g. sugar-reduced jams may ferment easily and go mouldy)

1 In countries such as the UK, why is it possible to have access to so many varied foods?

2 In a catering context, what does 'added value' mean?

4.3 COMBINING FOODS IN INDUSTRY

- identify the reasons for combining foods and varying ingredients in an industrial context
- understand the nutritional, aesthetic and economic effects of these practices

Food manufacturers combine foods and vary ingredients in a variety of ways to meet consumer demand for products to suit different lifestyles.

Added value

In an industrial context, added value may mean increasing the profit from basic raw materials by turning them into a variety of different products. e.g. turning potatoes into crisps, oven chips, waffles, etc., or turning sugar into a huge variety of confectionery. It may also mean improving the 'image' of the product by promoting its convenience (e.g. ready to eat), nutritional properties (e.g. reduced fat) or economy (e.g. feeds a family).

Reducing fat

Manufacturers have responded to consumer demand by producing a wide range of low fat and low sugar products.

Manufacturers reduce the fat content in their products by:
- □ adding water to products such as sausages and low-fat margarines
- □ using low-fat alternatives (e.g. yoghurt and skimmed milk) in products such as ice-cream, chocolate drinks and yoghurts
- □ removing more fat from meat joints and cuts.

Reducing sugar

The sugar content in products can be reduced or replaced by artificial sweeteners, e.g. aspartame and acesulfame.

Enhancing flavour

There are at least 4000 flavourings available to food manufacturers. Flavour modifiers or enhancers (e.g. monosodium glutamate) may be added to improve or reduce the flavour or smell of a food.

CHICKEN & LEEK SOUP

INGREDIENTS, WHEN RECONSTITUTED:
VEGETABLE (LEEK, ONION), WHEAT FLOUR, MODIFIED STARCH, HYDROGENATED VEGETABLE OIL, SALT, FLAVOURINGS, CHICKEN FAT, FLAVOUR ENHANCERS (MONOSODIUM GLUTAMATE, SODIUM GUANYLATE), STABILISER (SODIUM TRIPOLYPHOSPHATE), CASEINATES, SOY SAUCE, YEAST EXTRACT, SUGAR, HERBS, ACIDITY REGULATOR (SODIUM HYDROGEN ORTHOPHOSPHATE), SPICES, CITRIC ACID, ANTIOXIDANT (BHA)

NUTRITION INFORMATION - TYPICAL VALUES

	PER 100g	PER SERVING
ENERGY kJ	1751	350
kcal	418	84
PROTEIN	6.9g	1.4g
CARBOHYDRATE	54.1g	10.8g
FAT	19.3g	3.9g

Manufacturers are required by law to list the ingredients in a product on the packaging.

Important considerations

When combining ingredients, manufacturers have to consider:
- □ the effect on texture and storage, e.g. will reducing the fat content make a cake mixture too dry or reduce its shelf-life?
- □ is the addition of an ingredient (e.g. colouring) always necessary?
- □ does the addition of an ingredient (e.g. saffron) significantly increase the cost of a product?
- □ will the addition of an ingredient exclude part of the target group of consumers? (e.g. gelatine can be used to thicken yoghurt but it is made from animal bones and is not eaten by vegetarians).

---

1 How might a manufacturer reduce the fat content of the following:
   a) cheesecake b) lasagne c) oven-baked fish portions?

2 How might a food manufacturer give added value to improve the image of a product such as:
   a) a breakfast cereal b) a canned soup c) an instant coffee?

4.4 COMPONENTS USED IN FOOD MANUFACTURE

BY THE END OF THIS SECTION, YOU SHOULD BE ABLE TO:

- identify a variety of components that are commonly used and readily available to the food industry
- identify a variety of uses for these components
- suggest suitable equivalent components for use in catering

In common with other industries, the food industry uses **components** to manufacture its products. A component is an integral part of a manufactured product, e.g. a car has thousands of components, each one with a specific purpose. Likewise with food, each component, or **ingredient** performs a specific function.

Specialist manufacturers make components for other parts of the industry. For example, a factory will just make gear boxes or braking systems, which are then supplied in large numbers to the car factory. In the same way, parts of the food industry supply others with components.

Starch

One common ready-made component for use in manufacture of foods is modified starch which is used to fill out, bind, stabilize, thicken and alter the texture of processed foods e.g. soups, sauces, instant toppings, desserts and baby foods. Its equivalents in home cooking and catering include cornflour, wheat flour, starchy vegetables (e.g. potato, yam, cassava), rice, rice flour, soya flour, semolina, breadcrumbs and oatmeal.

Flavourings

Flavourings are also common components. They are either extracted from a plant or animal source (e.g. lemon oil and beef extract) or produced artificially in a laboratory by copying a particular flavouring chemical found naturally in a food (called **nature-identical flavourings**). Flavourings include herbs, spices, citrus fruit zest, stock, garlic, honey, vanilla, meat extractives, nut oils, ground nuts, butter, cheese, caramelized sugar, salt, pepper and vinegar.

Herbs, spices, colourings and flavourings are added to manufactured foods to supplement and enhance the natural flavour and colour of the ingredients in a product.

Fats and oils

Fats and oils (see Section 2.6) are components that are used in large quantities by the food industry, and can be modified by hydrogenation (see Section 3.12), blending, and heat processing to suit a variety of uses, including:

- deep fat frying at high temperatures, e.g. for the snack industry or take-away restaurants
- cake manufacture, where an easily mixed and incorporated fat component is required, with a high or low flavour and colour
- chocolate manufacture, e.g. with a higher melting point for products for export to hot countries, or a different consistency for cooking or confectionery chocolate (see Section 3.15)
- salad dressing manufacture, where pure, well-flavoured, and stable component oils are required for good shelf-life.

Combining components

In the food industry, basic components are often combined to form secondary components for use by manufacturers or in catering, for example: pastry; fruit pie fillings; pizza bases; cake icing and almond paste (marzipan); decorations and garnishes; cake, biscuit, scone and batter mixes; prepared fruit and vegetables (dried, canned or frozen).

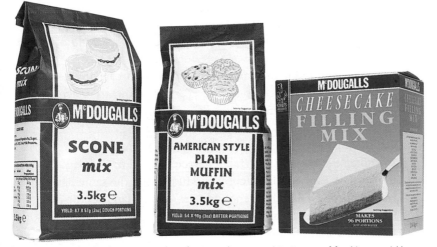

Caterers use ready-mixed components in order to produce a consistent range of food items quickly and cheaply.

Cost, time and quality control

There are both advantages and disadvantages to manufacturers in using food components made by other manufacturers. For example, frozen pastry used by the bakery section of a large supermarket gives a good result, saves preparation time and staff costs, saves buying raw materials, and saves energy and equipment. On the other hand it needs time to thaw, which must be allowed for in planning, it may be expensive and quality may vary between different suppliers so it must be monitored. Similarly dressings used by a sandwich manufacturer give a consistent result, save time, energy and raw materials and offer flavour variations. However their shelf-life may be too short to make it economical to buy them in bulk, they need cold storage, they may be expensive and quality may vary between different suppliers.

1 What is a component?

2 Why is it an advantage to a manufacturer of food products to buy particular components (e.g. pie fillings or tomato paste) in large quantities from other companies?

3 What do you think are the advantages to a food manufacturer of using nature-identical flavourings, e.g. almond or vanilla essence?

4 Why and how should a food manufacturer regularly check the quality of components purchased from other companies?

4.5 ADDITIVES (1)

BY THE END OF THIS SECTION, YOU SHOULD BE ABLE TO:

- understand why additives are used in food production
- understand the costs and benefits of using additives to both consumers and manufacturers
- understand what an E number is
- understand the different groups of additives and the foods in which they are used

'Instant' desserts contain artificial additives to provide extra colour and flavour.

Approximately 6 000 food additives (mainly flavourings) are used by the food manufacturing industry in the UK, amounting to about 200 000 tonnes of additives per year. More than three quarters of the food eaten in the UK has been processed, and most foods have additives in them.

Food manufacturers use additives for a variety of reasons, for example:

- ☐ to preserve foods and give them a prolonged shelf-life
- ☐ to improve the keeping qualities of food during processing, transport, distribution and retailing
- ☐ to produce food with uniform characteristics (shape, colour, flavour, texture, aroma) in a large-scale production
- ☐ to produce a food with characteristics that meet consumer expectations and associations, e.g. a certain colour to match a flavour, such as green for mint flavour
- ☐ to restore the original appearance of a food which may have been lost during processing, e.g. by adding colour
- ☐ to enhance (improve) a certain characteristic of a food, e.g. flavour
- ☐ to produce a variety of different products from the same basic ingredients by using different additives, e.g. instant noodle meals with different flavours
- ☐ to produce convenience foods for consumers whose lifestyle demands quick and easy meal preparation.

Requirements for the use of additives

The use of additives in food is controlled by government departments, including the Food Advisory Committee (FAC), the Ministry of Agriculture, Fisheries and Food (MAFF), and the Committee on Toxicity of Chemicals in Food, Consumer Products and the Environment (COT). There are many specific regulations controlling additive use, including for example, *The Preservatives in Food Regulations (1974)*, *The Sweeteners in Food Regulations (1983)* and *The Bread and Flour Regulations (1984)*.

The general principles which decide whether or not an additive can be permitted for use in food are as follows:

Safety

Food additives should be safe for consumers to eat. The effects of long-term consumption of additives are not clear but ongoing research into food safety suggests that some additives are harmful to the health of certain groups of people. Consumer groups have pressurized food manufacturers to review their use of additives, and to reduce or remove certain additives from their products.

Quantity

Additives should be used in the minimum amount required for them to do their job. There are laws governing the maximum amount of certain additives that can be safely used in foods. Over-use of additives may be harmful to consumers' health and uneconomic for the manufacturer.

DIABETIC FOODS

TANGERINE DELIGHT

Tangerine Flavour Dessert Mix
Just Add Milk

49 gram

Ingredients: Modified Starch, Whey Powder, Hydrogenerated Vegetable Oil, Emulsifiers (Propylene Glycol Monostearate, Lecithin), Gelling Agents (Disodium Monophosphate, Sodium Pyrophosphate), Milk Protien, Flavourings, Artificial Sweetener (*Aspartame), Colour (Apo-Carotene).

* Aspartame contains Phenylalanine.

The artificial sweetener aspartame is used in some foods for people who are diabetic and cannot eat sugar.

Labelling

Additives must be declared on the list of ingredients on a food label, in descending order of the amount used, and by name or 'E' number, except for flavourings. Some additives do not have to be declared if they are below certain levels, e.g. up to 15 g/litre of added sugar and 10 mg/litre of sulphur dioxide (preservative) can be added to fruit juices without the need for labelling. Some products, e.g. alcoholic drinks, unwrapped bread and cold cooked meats sold loose, do not list all their ingredients and may only state that they contain preservatives and colours without giving the individual names or E numbers.

Nutritional value

Additives should be of nutritional value to the body if possible. Some vitamins, e.g. vitamin C and beta-carotene, are used for a variety of purposes, including anti-oxidants and colourings. There are separate regulations for the nutritional labelling of food (see Section 8.7).

Misleading use of additives

The use of additives should not mislead consumers about the food in any way. There is some concern about the laws governing additives which enable manufacturers to add water to a food such as frozen chicken, fish and bacon. This adds weight to the product and increases the profit for the manufacturer but adds nothing to the nutritional value. The use of 'fillers' such as milk by-products, modified starches, sugar and fats which reduce the manufacturing cost are also the subject of concern for consumer protection groups.

MAKE - UP INSTRUCTIONS

Remove lid. Add boiling water up to the fill level and stir well. Allow to stand for 3 minutes. Top up to the fill level with boiling water if necessary and stir again before serving.

INGREDIENTS

NOODLES, CORNSTARCH, MALTODEXTRIN, FLAVOURINGS, DRIED GLUCOSE SYRUP, FLAVOUR ENHANCER: MONOSODIUM GLUTAMATE; TEXTURED VEGETABLE PROTEIN (WITH DEFATTED SOYA FLOUR, SALT, HYDROLYSED VEGETABLE PROTEIN, FLAVOUR ENHANCERS: MONOSODIUM GLUTAMATE, SODIUM-5'RIBONUCLEOTIDE; FLAVOURINGS), HYDROGENATED VEGETABLE OIL, ONION POWDER, HYDROLYSED VEGETABLE PROTEIN, SALT, DRIED MUSHROOM, DRIED PEAS, SUGAR, DRIED CARROT, COLOUR: PLAIN CARAMEL; SODIUM CASEIMATES, DRIED PARSLEY, ACIDITY REGULATOR: DIPOTASSIUM HYDROGEN ORTHOPHOSPHATE

NUTRITION INFORMATION

TYPICAL VALUES (MADE UP AS PER INSTRUCTIONS) PER 100g (3.5 oz): ENERGY 331 k J., 78 k cal; PROTEIN 2.6g; CARBOHYDRATE 14.5g of which SUGARS 2.4g STARCH 12.1g; FAT 1.1g of which SATURATES 0.4g; FIBRE 0.1g; SODIUM 0.6g.

PER POT   212 CALORIES   2.4g FAT

Pot noodles are an 'instant meal' consisting of basic noodles supplemented by various flavourings and fillers.

1 Give five reasons why additives are used in the manufacture of food products.

2 Which of the following products do you think is likely to have the most flavouring added to it:
a) a strawberry yoghurt
b) a banana flavour yoghurt
c) a mandarin orange flavoured yoghurt?

3 Why are there strict rules about the use of additives in food products?

4 Why are many people and consumer groups opposed to the widespread use of food additives?

5 Which major group of additives has not as yet been allocated E numbers, and only has to be listed under its group name on food labels?

4.5 ADDITIVES (2)

BY THE END OF THIS SECTION, YOU SHOULD BE ABLE TO:

- understand why additives are used in food production
- understand the costs and benefits of using additives to both consumers and manufacturers
- understand what an E number is
- understand the different groups of additives and the foods in which they are used

Some of the additives used by food manufacturers have an **E number** to identify them. The E number indicates that the additive has been approved for use throughout the European Union.

Classification of food additives			
Name	**Use**	**Examples**	**E number**
Acids	often used as preservatives	lactic acid tartaric acid	270 334
Acidity regulators	to control acidity or alkalinity	acetic acid calcium lactate citric acid	260 327 330
Anti-caking agents	to stop particles sticking together	calcium carbonate silicon dioxide	170 551
Anti-foaming agents	to stop excessive foaming when making and using jam, syrup, soft drinks	dimethylpolysiloxane	900
Anti-oxidants	to prevent rancidity, discoloration, caused by oxidation	l-ascorbic acid sulphur dioxide	300 220
Colours	to enhance appearance	curcumin tartrazine amaranth annatto betanin	100 102 123 160(b) 162
Emulsifiers	to prevent oil and water separating	lecithins carob gum gum arabic	322 410 414
Firming agents	to keep tissues of fruit or vegetables firm when canning	calcium citrate calcium sulphate	333 516
Flavour enhancers	to enhance an existing flavour without adding flavouring	monosodium glutamate	621

Green colouring is often used in conjunction with mint flavouring.

Pork Salami Sausage

Ingredients: Pork, Salt, Spices, Dextrose, Flavour enhancer: E621, Maltodextrin, Preservative: sodium nitrate. Not less than 100% meat.

Barbecue Marinade

INGREDIENTS: Sugar, Salt, Tomato Powder, Flavourings, Rusk, Yeast Extract, Modified Starch, Garlic Powder, Stabiliser (E464), Anti-caking Agents (E551, E341c), Chili Powder, Citric Acid, Cumin, Paprika Extract, Colours (E150, E120).

Name	Use	Examples	E number
Foam stabilizers	to keep bubbles evenly distributed in e.g. ice-cream	propylene glycol alginate	405
Gelling agents	to give texture to instant puddings, soya milk, fruit pie, fillings	agar carrageenan locust bean gum pectin	406 407 410 440(a)
Glazing agents	to give shiny coating to tablets or sweets	beeswax shellac	901 904
Humectants	to stop foods drying out, e.g. soft centres of chocolates	sorbitol mannitol	420(i) 421
Modified starches	used in packet soups, baby foods, desserts	starch treated by acid, alkali, bleach	No numbers
Packaging gases	to preserve packs of e.g. fish, nuts	nitrogen	No numbers
Preservatives	to prolong shelf-life	sorbic acid potassium sorbate benzoic acid sodium benzoate potassium nitrate	200 202 210 211 252
Raising agents	to raise baked goods	sodium hydrogen carbonate	500
Sequesterants	to prevent 'off-flavours' and discoloration in e.g. fruit, fish	calcium citrate calcium sulphate	333 516
Stabilizers	to help keep a product the same condition as when it was produced	tri-sodium citrate tragacanth	331(c) 413
Sweeteners	to add sweetness to product without using sucrose	sorbitol aspartame saccharin acesulfame potassium	420 No numbers
Thickeners	to increase the viscosity of a product	alginic acid carrageenan pectin	400 407 440(a)

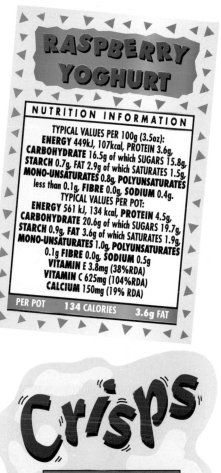

1 What is an E number?

2 Give examples of additives used for:
   a) colouring
   b) enhancing flavour
   c) glazing.

3 Find out what a 'permitted list' of additives is.

4 Why is calcium lactate (E327) added to products such as marmalade and jams?

4.6 ACIDS AND ALKALIS

BY THE END OF THIS SECTION, YOU SHOULD BE ABLE TO:

- understand the differences between acids and alkalis
- understand the effects of these on the appearance, texture, flavour, nutritional value and safety of food

Citrus fruits are very acidic.

Lemon juice (citric acid) is an anti-oxidant. It can be used to stop apples oxidizing and turning brown when cut.

Acid and alkalis are measured on a **pH scale**.

0	1	2	3	4	5	6	7	8	9	10	11	12	13	14
		ACID									ALKALINE			

stronger   weaker   neutral   weaker   stronger
(not acid or alkaline)

Acids and alkalis are found in many different kinds of food.

Acids in foods	
Name	**Examples of where found**
ascorbic acid (vitamin C)	oranges, lemons, grapefruit, potatoes, cabbage, beansprouts, used as an additive (E300)
citric acid	lemons, oranges, used as an additive (E330)
ethanoic acid (acetic acid)	vinegar
lactic acid	sour milk, used as an additive (E270)
folate, nicotinic acid,	vitamins found in various foods
Alkalis in foods	
Name	**Examples of where found**
bicarbonate of soda	baked items, e.g. cakes

The properties of acids

Some acids can be used to stop foods reacting with oxygen. They are known as **anti-oxidants**. For example, some types of fruit go brown when cut and exposed to oxygen in the air, and the acid in lemon juice (citric acid) can be used to stop this reaction. Ascorbic acid added to foods helps stop fat going 'off' (rancid) when exposed to air. L-Tartaric acid (E334) and l-ascorbic acid (E300) are permitted anti-oxidants used commercially.

Some acids are used to give a sour or sharp taste to food, such as citrus fruits or vinegar.

Acids are often used to denature protein, for example:

- lemon juice added to milk causes the protein caseinogen to clot, so lemon juice added to cream and condensed milk can be used to set the filling for a lemon flan
- marinading meat in vinegar or orange juice helps to tenderize it
- ascorbic acid added to flour improves the quality of the gluten in bread-making, so l-ascorbic acid (E300) is often used as a commercial flour improver
- vinegar or tartaric acid added to meringue helps to stabilize it

Corrosion effects

Acids have a corrosive effect on metals and other substances. Acidic canned fruits, e.g. oranges and tomatoes, will react with metal, so cans must be lined with a plastic coating. Acids produced by the action of bacteria on sugar in the mouth dissolve tooth enamel and cause decay.

Acidity and setting

Citric acid (E330) is used in commercial jam-making to extract the natural pectin from the fruit which makes the jam set (see Section 4.1).

Preservatives

Another reason acids are used in food manufacture is because they have a preservative effect on foods. For example, vinegar (pH 2–3) will prevent the growth of bacteria (which grow at pH 7), and yeasts (which grow at pH 4–4.5), while lactic acid in the muscles of slaughtered animals helps to preserve meat. Sorbic acid (E200), benzoic acid (E210), lactic acid (E270) and propionic acid (E280) are all used as permitted preservatives (see Section 4.5).

Acids are also used to neutralize the effects of alkalis. For example, bicarbonate of soda (sodium hydrogen carbonate) used alone as a raising agent in baking leaves a yellow, soapy-tasting residue. Cream of tartar (potassium hydrogen tartrate) is a weak acid which is used to neutralize this reaction so the resulting raising agent is colourless and tasteless. Bicarbonate of soda and cream of tartar are the main ingredients of baking powder.

The properties of alkalis

Alkalis are used to act as a raising agent, for example, bicarbonate of soda which produces carbon dioxide gas when heated. They also neutralize the effects of acids. Sodium, calcium and ammonium hydroxides are used commercially to neutralize acids. For example, sodium hydroxide neutralizes free fatty acids in the manufacture of cooking oils, while calcium hydroxide is used to neutralize acid in beer-making.

Buffers

In order to maintain the correct acid–alkali balance in commercially manufactured foods, substances called **buffers** are added e.g. calcium lactate – E327 and sodium citrate – E331.

Baking powder contains both an acid (cream of tartar) and an alkali (bicarbonate of soda).

1 What numbers on the pH scale indicate acids?

2 Name three acids and give examples of which foods they are found in.

3 Find out the names of six food products which have anti-oxidants E334 and E300 added to them.

4 Why are cans of mandarin oranges lined with plastic?

5 Why is baking powder added to plain flour to make items such as scones and cakes?

6 Why are acidic foods often served with fatty foods (e.g. apple sauce with pork, lemon with fried fish)?

7 Why do you think it is unnecessary to add cream of tartar to the bicarbonate of soda when making gingerbread?

8 How does a chilled lemon flan made with fresh lemons, cream and condensed milk, thicken?

4.7 THE USES OF PACKAGING

BY THE END OF THIS SECTION, YOU SHOULD BE ABLE TO:

- understand the functions of packaging in food products
- identify the main types of materials used in packaging

Packaging has a number of functions. It protects the product from the outside environment including dust, insects, animals, odours, fumes, humidity (amount of moisture in the air), oxygen, light, temperature changes, people and contamination by chemicals or physical objects. At the same time it protects the outside environment from the product, e.g. leakage or spillage, odours, colour stains. It also prevents damage to a product through transport and handling by consumers. Packaging helps prolong the shelf-life of a product by slowing down or preventing natural decay and spoilage by micro-organisms.

An important function of packaging is to provide consumers with information including product name and description, weight, size or volume of product, instructions for use and storage, nutritional information, list of ingredients, name and address of producer, country of origin of product, 'use by' or 'best before' date. It also helps to advertise the product and promote the manufacturer.

Packaging materials

Manufacturers have a large number of packaging materials to choose from, and often combine two or more types to package a product.

Plastics

A large number of plastics are available. They are made from oil and therefore are a finite resource, but some can be recycled. Plastic is lightweight, but is relatively strong. It can be rigid (stiff) or flexible, and can be made into a variety of shapes and sizes. Plastic can be coloured, opaque or transparent, and can be printed. Most plastics do not react with foods (they are inert) and can prevent moisture coming into or out of a product. Some can prevent oxygen and other gases coming into or out of a product.

Examples of plastic packaging include:

- PVC (polyvinyl chloride): plastic trays, bottles for non-carbonated drinks and vegetable oils
- high-density polythene: milk and fruit juice bottles
- low-density polythene: polythene bags and films
- PET (polyethylene terephthalate): bottles for carbonated drinks and cooking oils
- CPET (crystalline polyethylene terephthalate): in this form the molecules exist in a more organized structure that enables the plastic to be heated up to 200°C, so it is used for containers for ready meals
- polystyrene: yoghurt, meat
- polypropylene: biscuit wrappings, snack and sweet bags.

Cardboard and paper

Cardboard and paper are made from a renewable resource and can be recycled. They can be coloured and printed very successfully, and can be made into a variety of shapes by cutting, creasing, folding and gluing. However, they cannot prevent moisture, oxygen, or gases coming into or out of a product unless they are laminated with plastic or metal foil.

Plastic bottles make useful lightweight containers.

Cardboard has to be lined or coated to prevent the food from coming into contact with it.

Examples of cardboard and paper packaging include:

- cardboard boxes and band wrappers for breakfast cereals; sweets and chocolates; biscuits; tea; pasta; ready meals; pet foods; cartons of fruit juice or milk; take-away foods (e.g. pizzas) and cakes and pastries
- paper bags and sachets for flour; loose-sold items (e.g. fruit); dried sauce mixes; powdered gelatine; tea and coffee bags; packet cake, pastry, biscuit and batter mixes; dried herb and spice refills.

Glass

Glass can by recycled. It is strong but can break. Glass prevents loss or gain of moisture and oxygen or other gases. It can be coloured, transparent or opaque and can be printed, or have transfers or labels attached. It can be made into a wide variety of shapes and sizes. Glass does not react with food.

Glass is used to make bottles and jars for jam and preserves, sauces and pickles, instant coffee, alcoholic and non-alcoholic drinks and fresh milk.

Glass does not react with food.

Metal

Steel and aluminium are the most common metals used for food packaging. Aluminium is lighter than steel. Metals can be recycled and are rigid and strong, but can be dented. Metal prevents loss or gain of moisture, oxygen or other gases, but the surface must be properly sealed as some metals react with foods. They can be coated with plastic to prevent this. Metals containers can be printed or labelled, and foil in particular can be made into a variety of shapes and sizes.

Metallized films can be made by vaporizing aluminium onto the surface of paper or plastic, and are used to package crisps, snacks, sweets, biscuits and cakes. Metal can also be used to laminate paper and card cartons to package liquids such as long-life juice, soup, milk and cream.

Metal cans are used for carbonated and still drinks, fruit, vegetables, meat, fish, sauces, puddings, milk and cream.

Aluminium foil and coated plastic are used extensively for food packaging.

1 Why is clear labelling important, and what information should it give the consumer?

2 Why are plastics used so much by the packaging industry?

3 What are the advantages and disadvantages of using the following as packaging materials:
a) glass b) paper and cardboard c) metals?

4 Why does packaging cause concern to consumers and environmentalists?

5 What steps are being taken by manufacturers and local councils to meet these concerns?

4.8 HEAT (1)

- understand how heat passes from one object to another
- identify examples of this in the production of food
- identify how the nutrients, texture, flavour, aroma, appearance and safety of foods are affected by heat

Heat energy passes from one object to another in three ways: **conduction**, **convection** and **radiation**.

Conduction

Heat energy vibrates the molecules of an object. The neighbouring molecules then vibrate and pass the heat energy on to others. **Good conductors** of heat, such as metals, pass the energy quickly. For this reason, jacket potatoes cook more quickly if a metal skewer is placed inside them during baking. Similarly, flat, solid metal-based pans conduct heat most efficiently. **Poor conductors** of heat such as cloth, wood, plastic, glass and still

A metal skewer conducts heat through the potatoes.

air pass heat energy slowly. They act as **insulators** by preventing heat energy from passing through them easily. For this reason, items cooked in ceramic or glass oven dishes take longer to cook, and insulated cool boxes keep food cool for several hours.

Convection

Heat energy causes molecules in a liquid or gas to expand and rise. Convection currents are set up as the colder liquid falls and is heated in turn. The movement of the molecules passes on the heat energy.

Foods which are baked, boiled or steamed are heated by convection. Some foods with slow convection currents, e.g. sauces, have to be stirred to prevent burning.

Radiation

Energy can be transmitted by **electromagnetic waves**, e.g. infra-red rays (heat energy), ultra-violet rays (light) and microwaves. Heat energy in the form of **infra-red rays** passes from one object to another without heating the space between them. Grilled and spit-roasted foods are partly cooked by radiation. Barbecued food is heated by radiation from glowing charcoal. Dark, dull surfaces absorb and **emit** (give off) infra-red rays, while light, shiny surfaces reflect heat rays. This is why light coloured delivery vehicles are used to help keep foods cool during transport.

Microwaves vibrate millions of times per second. When absorbed by food, they vibrate the water molecules in it, causing friction and then heat to be produced to cook the food. Microwaves are reflected by metal objects and absorbed by food. Microwaves pass through, but do not heat up, materials such as ceramics, glass and some plastics.

Meat cooked on a barbecue is heated by the heat radiating off the glowing charcoal.

Effects of heat on foods

Different sorts of heat used to cook food will produce different results. For example, if a sponge pudding is baked in the oven, it will have a golden brown crust, with a lighter coloured centre. If it is steamed or microwaved, it will be light coloured with only a thin crust.

Protein

The chemical structure of protein is permanently changed by heat. The protein eventually solidifies. For example, if an egg is heated, the transparent 'white' becomes opaque and solid, while the yolk gradually becomes firm and eventually dry. When meat is heated, the collagen and elastin contract and the meat shrinks. Overheating causes meat to become hard and indigestible. However, the collagen will change to gelatine if moisture is present, and the meat will become tender. When heated, the gluten in wheat flour sets. This forms the structure of bread, cakes, pastries and biscuits.

Heat makes the protein in an egg change its chemical structure so that the egg solidifies.

Carbohydrate

Starch

Dry heat changes starch to **dextrin** when toasting bread or baking cakes, biscuits and bread, for example. Wet heat causes starch granules to absorb water, soften and swell. Some of the granules then break and release starch which forms a stiff gel. This process is called gelatinization (see Section 4.1). It occurs in sauce-making, boiling starchy root vegetables, and boiling rice and other cereal grains in water.

Sugar (sucrose)

Dry heat causes sugar to melt, then **caramelize** (go brown in colour), when grilling the sugar topping on a crème brûlée, for example. Eventually the sugar will burn, leaving a black carbon residue. Wet heat dissolves sugar to a syrup, which will eventually caramelize. This process is used in toffee and caramel making, baking cakes and biscuits, making crème caramel, praline or spun sugar. A black, carbon residue is left when all the water has evaporated.

---

1   How is heat conducted from a cooker hob to butter melting in a pan?

2   Why are metal casserole dishes more efficient at conducting heat than glass ones?

3   Why is it important to stir a sauce while it is being heated?

4   Why is it important not to use metallic dishes in a microwave oven?

5   Why does:
   a) meat shrink in size when cooked
   b) egg change from a runny texture to solid when cooked
   c) cake mixture set when baked?

4.8 HEAT (2)

BY THE END OF THIS SECTION, YOU SHOULD BE ABLE TO:

- understand how heat passes from one object to another
- identify examples of this in the production of food
- identify how the nutrients, texture, flavour, aroma, appearance and safety of foods are affected by heat

Vitamins

Fat-soluble vitamins

Vitamins A, D, E and K are mostly unaffected by normal cooking temperatures.

Water-soluble vitamins

B group Thiamin (B1) is destroyed by high cooking temperatures. Riboflavin (B2) is destroyed if heated with alkali. Folate (folic acid – vitamin B complex) becomes unstable if heated with acid. Pryridoxine (B6) and nicotinic acid (niacin) are unaffected by normal cooking temperatures.

Ascorbic acid

Another name for Vitamin C, this is easily and quickly destroyed by heat.

Raising of flour mixtures

Heat causes gases to expand. Air can be trapped in the flour mixture by creaming, beating, whisking, rolling or folding. The trapped air will expand and cause the mixture to rise when heated, as will any gas which is produced during cooking. For example, carbon dioxide gas is produced by baking powder, bicarbonate of soda or yeast, while water vapour (steam) is produced in items such as batters and choux pastry.

Protein and carbohydrate

When protein is heated with carbohydrate, a series of reactions can occur which results in browning. This is called a **Maillard reaction** and occurs during the baking and toasting of breakfast cereals and roasted nuts.

Fat

Solid fat melts to liquid oil and the process is reversed on cooling. These changes can be observed in melted chocolate, biscuit flan bases and dripping from roasted meat. Continued heating raises the temperature of fat, until at high temperatures above 200°C fat molecules start to break down, releasing **free fatty acids**. These affect flavour and keeping qualities.

Hot oil is used in deep and shallow frying. If the oil continues to be heated, a blue haze is given off which then turns to smoke and taints the food. Eventually the oil will reach 'flash point' when it will ignite and burn fiercely. It gives off black carbon smoke and a huge sheet of flame which is extremely dangerous.

Burning fat is extremely dangerous.

Flavour and aroma

Flavours are developed in some foods during heating or spoiled in others. For example, green vegetables can become bitter if overcooked and spices may intensify (strengthen) during cooking.

Aromas are given off and travel in the air when food is cooked. Many foods are easily identifiable by their aromas alone, e.g. freshly baked bread, roasted coffee beans, roasted pork, grilled cheese, fried fish, grilled bacon and caramelized sugar.

Colour

Heat causes changes in colour in a variety of foods. Different types of heat result in different colours in the same food. Boiled green vegetables are bright green at the start of cooking, but become dark olive green then brown after prolonged boiling. Red meat becomes brown as heat changes the protein structure.

If green vegetables are cooked for too long they turn an unappetizing colour.

Micro organisms

Most micro-organisms are destroyed by heating to 100°C. For example, yeast is destroyed above 55°C (see Section 8.2). Heat is used in many types of food preservation to prevent or delay microbial growth, e.g. canning, sterilization and pasteurization.

1 What will happen to Brussels sprouts, green cabbage and broccoli if they are boiled for half an hour?

2 Why is it important that canned food manufacturers ensure that products such as meat pie fillings, chicken and fish are thoroughly heated to the correct temperature and for the correct time?

3 What do you think is the cause of the following and how can each be prevented:
   a) sticky, 'gluey' rice that stays in large lumps instead of separate grains
   b) a baked jacket potato that is still crunchy in the centre
   c) tough, dry and chewy meat that has been grilled
   d) tough, dense, poorly risen bread?

4.9 COLD

Peas are frozen immediately after they are harvested so they have a higher nutritional value than those which have to be transported to shops and stored before they reach the consumer.

Chilling drinks by adding ice to them when they are served adds to the flavour and enjoyment.

Food is chilled or frozen in order to give it a longer shelf-life, preserve it, change its texture and appearance and improve its flavour.

Food safety

Micro-organisms tend to be most active in warm temperatures. As the temperature drops, the activity slows down and eventually stops (they become **dormant**). Some micro-organisms die in the cold, but most become active again once the temperature rises.

Chilling in a refrigerator extends the shelf-life of most food by several days. Freezing food preserves most foods for several weeks or months by keeping micro-organisms dormant and stopping natural decay.

Food manufacturers are required to give clear instructions to consumers about the safe storage of chilled and frozen foods.

Texture and appearance

Cold changes the texture and appearance of many foods.

Fats which have been melted to become oils will **solidify** when chilled. This also applies to foods that are high in fat, e.g. chocolate and cheese.

Gelatine is used to make some foods solidify when cooled (see Section 4.1).

Water in food turns into crystals of ice when frozen. Ice crystals which form inside the cells of fruits, vegetables and meat may cause the cells to rupture. Once the food thaws, the water will be released, the cells will collapse, and the food may lose its original texture as happens with strawberries. Some foods, e.g. ice-cream and sorbets, depend on the formation of ice crystals to give them their characteristics.

Flavour and enjoyment

Several types of food are more refreshing when chilled, e.g. fruit juices, chilled soups, salads and fresh fruit such as melon.

The flavours of some foods, e.g. meat sauces containing curry spices or garlic, become stronger after chilling for several hours. The flavours of other foods, such as cheeses, become more recognizable if they are allowed to stand at room temperature for an hour before serving.

Refrigeration

When a liquid **evaporates**, it absorbs heat. Refrigerators have a liquid (the **refrigerant**) which flows round tubes inside and at the back. The refrigerant absorbs heat from the food put into the refrigerator and the food cools down. The absorbed heat vaporizes the refrigerant which condenses to a liquid again when the vapour flows into the tubes at the back (you can feel the heat given off). Then the whole process starts again.

Foods should be refrigerated:

- by food manufacturers before distribution
- by distributors in refrigerated ships, planes and lorries
- in shops in refrigerated display cabinets
- in commercial kitchens in restaurants
- by mobile food vendors and in vending machines
- by consumers in domestic refrigerators.

Food hygiene laws (see Section 8.5) stipulate the range of temperatures at which refrigerated foods must be held to reduce the risk of food poisoning.

The development of **cook-chill ready meals** has caused some concern about food safety. The food is cooked in order to kill harmful bacteria. It is then rapidly chilled and kept cold to prevent bacterial growth. If the temperature rises during transport or storage, there may be a risk of food poisoning. Manufacturers must give storage instructions (including the temperature) on products that require refrigeration. Consumers should check that their refrigerator is cold enough to store the food safely.

Some foods are held in cold storage in an atmosphere of carbon dioxide gas. This is often referred to as **controlled atmosphere (CA) storage**. This slows down the growth of micro-organisms, and is used for foods such as eggs, apples, pears, root vegetables and meat.

Freezing

The principle and process of freezing are the same as for refrigeration, but the temperatures used are much lower. Smaller ice crystals are formed and therefore cause less damage to food if it is frozen quickly. The flavours of some foods become stronger and others become weaker during storage in a freezer. The nutritional value of foods is mostly unaffected by freezing. Some quick frozen foods, e.g. commercially frozen peas, are likely to contain more vitamin C than fresh ones which may lose nutrients during transport, storage and preparation.

Commercial freezing

Food manufacturers use a variety of methods to fast-freeze their products. In one method, cold air is blown over food. In **multi-plate freezers** products are packed in flat containers and pressed tightly between hollow, flat metal plates which are refrigerated. Some food is immersed in or sprayed with liquid nitrogen which is extremely cold. This is called **cryogenic freezing**. Frozen food should be completely defrosted (thawed out) before it is cooked.

1 Why is food chilled or frozen?

2 How do the following foods set when they are chilled:
   a) chocolate rice cakes
   b) ice-cream
   c) jelly?

3 Why are some foods unsuitable for freezing? Give reasons and examples.

4 Why are consumers advised to keep certain products refrigerated once opened, and to use them within a few days?

5 Why are there very strict hygiene rules about the manufacture and sale of cook-chill foods?

6 How do refrigerators chill food?

The coldest part of a refrigerator should be between these temperatures — 5 to 0

Temperature of icebox in a * refrigerator — -5 -6

Temperature of icebox in a * * refrigerator — 12 -15

Usual temperature range of frozen food display cabinets in shops – must be no higher than -12°C and not overfilled — -10

Temperature of icebox in a * * * refrigerator — -18 -20

A wholesaler's cold room should be between these temperatures for frozen food storage — -25

Temperature at which food should be frozen and stored in a factory — -30

It is important to hold frozen and chilled foods at the right temperature.

4.10 REMOVAL OF MOISTURE

Micro-organisms need moisture to enable them to grow and reproduce. The removal of moisture (**dehydration**) helps to preserve food, and was one of the first methods of preservation to be used.

Moisture is removed by a process called **osmosis**. Osmosis is the movement of water from a weak solution to a strong solution, through a semi-permeable membrane.

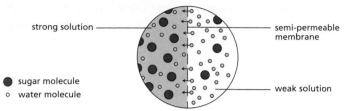

Water moves from a weak solution to a strong solution by osmosis.

When food is dehydrated, the concentration of sugars and salts in the food increases. If there are any micro-organisms in the food, water will pass from their cells (a dilute solution) into the more concentrated solution surrounding them. Deprived of water, the micro-organisms cannot grow and are destroyed.

The food will stay dehydrated until water is put back (**rehydrated**), then the situation will be reversed. Once water is put back into food, micro-organisms will start to grow and reproduce again. Dried food must therefore be stored in a cool, dry place.

Methods of dehydration

Sun-drying

This traditional method of leaving food out in the sun is still used for some foods, e.g. tomatoes and dried fruit.

Hot-air bed

Solid foods, e.g. meat, are put onto perforated trays. Hot air is blown through the trays under carefully controlled conditions regulating the time and temperature.

Spray-drying

Spray-drying is used for liquid foods, e.g. milk. The finely sprayed food is blown into a hot air chamber, where it dries as granules and drops to the bottom for collection.

Accelerated freeze-drying

Liquid food, e.g. coffee, is frozen very rapidly. Tiny ice crystals form in the food. These are quickly removed by turning them to vapour, as the food is heated in a vacuum.

Dried fruit can be rehydrated by soaking it in water for about 12 hours.

The effects of dehydration

Colour

The colour of the food may change completely when dehydrated, e.g. green grapes turn to brown sultanas or currants. The food may darken because it becomes concentrated as it dries.

Texture

Food may become brittle, as in dried herbs, or it may become hard, as in dried pulses and peas, or it may crumble, as in freeze-dried coffee granules.

Appearance

Food may wrinkle, e.g. dried plums (prunes). It will shrink in size and become lighter in weight.

Sultanas and currants are produced by dehydrating seedless grapes.

Flavour

Drying concentrates food, which may become sweeter or more salty as a result. The heat may alter some of the characteristics of the food, e.g. the protein and carbohydrates, and therefore change the flavour.

Nutrients

Some vitamins, e.g. vitamin C and thiamin, may be destroyed.

Additives

Some dry foods, e.g. salt and icing sugar, have **anti-caking agents** such as tri-calcium diorthophosphate E341 added to help them flow freely.

Some foods, e.g. confectionery and cake icing, have **humectants** such as aglycerol E422 or sorbitol E420 added to prevent them from drying out and becoming hard. Humectants absorb water vapour from the air.

1 Why do micro-organisms need moisture?

2 How were foods dehydrated to preserve them in the past?

3 Why is it important to prevent dried foods from becoming damp?

4 What happens to the appearance and texture of the following fresh foods when they are dried:
a) apricots b) peas c) parsley d) milk?

5 What is osmosis and how does it remove moisture from foods?

6 How are dried foods rehydrated?

7 Why are dried foods such as sultanas or apricots sweeter than fresh ones?

8 What are humectants and why are they used?

4.11 REMOVAL OF AIR AND OXIDATION

Vacuum packed food will not deteriorate quickly as it is not exposed to air.

Some micro-organisms can only grow and reproduce **aerobically** (when oxygen is present). The colour of some foods such as fresh meat, changes in the presence of air.

It is possible to prevent or slow down the growth of aerobic micro-organisms, and extend the shelf-life of certain foods, e.g. fish, meat, vegetables, fruit, ready-made meals and fresh pasta, by:

- removing all air from around the food by **vacuum-packaging**
- replacing the oxygen with special mixtures of gases in **modified atmosphere packaging (MAP)** and **controlled atmosphere packaging (CAP)**.

Foods packaged in this way can be kept unopened for several weeks (according to the manufacturer's storage instructions).

Potential problems with micro-organisms

Some micro-organisms can grow and reproduce **anaerobically** (without oxygen), such as the bacterium which causes **botulism,** a severe form of food poisoning which is often fatal. It is not easy to detect the growth of bacteria by sight, smell or flavour, and the food may appear to be perfectly safe to eat. If the food is not properly heat-treated before packaging, or is incorrectly stored, anaerobic micro-organisms may grow and reproduce in such numbers that they cause food poisoning.

If the package develops even a tiny leak, and air is allowed in, aerobic micro-organisms will be able to develop and may cause food poisoning.

Oxidation

Oxidation is a process where a substance reacts and becomes combined with oxygen from the air. There are several serious consequences as a result of oxidation in foods.

Rancidity

Foods rich in fat, especially fat with a high percentage of poly-unsaturated fatty acids, can 'go off' and develop bad flavours and odours, which may cause sickness if the food is eaten. This is because the fat reacts with oxygen from the air during storage. This type of oxidation is called rancidity.

Rancidity is speeded up by the food being exposed to light, exposed to metal, or repeatedly heated up as with oil for deep frying.

Examples of foods which can become rancid include: wholemeal flour (fat in the wheatgerm), cooking oils, margarines, cooking fats and meat.

Colour of red meat

After slaughter, meat has a dark red colour, but when cut and exposed to the air, it changes to bright red, because of the oxidation of **myoglobin** which is a purple/dark red substance found in muscle. Myoglobin reacts with oxygen to become **oxymyoglobin** which gives the cut surface of the meat a bright red appearance.

Meat changes from dark red to bright red when it is cut and exposed to air.

Colour of fruit and vegetables

When certain fruits and vegetables, e.g. bananas, apples and potatoes, are cut and exposed to air, they become brown in colour. This is due to oxidation and is speeded up by the natural **oxidase enzymes** which they contain. Storing the food under water with lemon juice in it reduces browning.

Destruction of vitamin C

Vitamin C is very easily destroyed by oxidation and becomes useless to the body as a result. Destruction is speeded up if foods containing vitamin C are cut finely and left exposed to the air for a while before they are eaten.

Preventing oxidation

Oxidation can be prevented or slowed down by the following means.

Correct packaging

Fatty foods should be stored in paper, cardboard or plastic packaging that allows as little oxygen or light to pass through it as possible.

Blanching

Fruits and vegetables to be frozen are often **blanched** (briefly exposed to boiling water), to destroy oxidase enzymes which would lead to browning.

Correct storage and preparation

Fatty foods should be used by the date recommended by the manufacturer. They should be stored away from light and air. Fruit and vegetables should be cut up just before eating.

Anti-oxidants

Anti-oxidants are substances which prevent oxidation. Some natural anti-oxidants, e.g. vitamin E, are found in foods such as plant oils. Chemical anti-oxidants are added to foods by manufacturers (see table).

The vitamin C content of fruit is destroyed if the fruit is cut open and left exposed to air.

Permitted anti-oxidants	
l-ascorbic acid (vitamin C)	E300
tocopherol (vitamin E)	E306
butylated hydroxyanisole (BHA)	E320

1 How does the removal of air help to preserve some foods?

2 Why must the packaging of vacuum-packed foods be tough and be completely sealed?

3 Why is correct heat treatment of such products essential?

4 Why do bananas and apples go brown when exposed to the air?

5 Why is it not advisable to cut cabbage finely and leave it on a chopping board for an hour before cooking it?

6 Why is it advisable to store wholemeal flour in a sealed container in a dark, cool and dry cupboard?

7 Find out and name six products that have anti-oxidants added to them, e.g. E300, E306 and E320.

8 Why are poly-unsaturated fats more likely to go rancid than saturated fats?

9 Why are cooking fats often sold in opaque plastic or paper packaging?

10 How does blanching prevent oxidation?

4.12 TOOLS AND EQUIPMENT

In food manufacturing and catering ingredients are mixed in large quantities by powerful machines.

Mixers and blenders

Mixers, blenders and food processors save time in food preparation. They are used in both domestic and industrial kitchens.

A machine should have the following features.

☐ It should have the power and capacity to do a range of jobs.

☐ It should be easy to keep clean.

☐ It should be made of a suitable and durable material.

☐ It should be easy to fit and use attachments.

☐ The bowl of the mixer should be deep enough so that the ingredients will not be thrown out during mixing.

Attachments: dough hook, blender, electric can-opener, mincer, potato peeler, juice extractor, slicer and shredder, bean slicer, sieve.

Blenders (liquidizers)

Blenders have a variety of uses, including soup making, puréeing fruit and vegetables, mixing batters, chopping nuts, herbs, breadcrumbs, and blending mayonnaise and salad dressings.

Food processors

Food processors carry out a wide range of tasks, including finely chopping or slicing fruit and herbs, meat and cheese. They can also be used for chopping fat into flour for pastry, making breadcrumbs, grinding whole wheat, peeling vegetables and puréeing food.

Pans

A well equipped kitchen should have a range of pans including: milk saucepan with a lip for easy pouring, frying pan, wok, vegetable saucepans, egg poacher, tiered steamer/casserole, pressure cooker and skillet (shallow pan with lid).

Pans can be made from stainless steel, aluminium, or enamelled iron or steel. They can also be made from special heat-tolerant glass or ceramic. **Stainless steel** will not chip or flake. It is strong, durable, resistant to rust, little affected by chemical reactions so that it does not stain, and it does not give food a metallic taste. Pans with metal such as copper welded on to the base heat up more quickly, but they are more expensive.

Once stainless steel heats up, it holds the heat well, the hob burner or hot-plate can be turned down to keep the contents cooking evenly without wasting fuel. **Aluminium** is cheaper to produce than stainless steel, and lighter. However, it is not as strong and is discoloured by certain foods. **Enamelled steel or cast iron** can be made into attractive coloured pans. They conduct heat quite rapidly, but are inclined to discolour and chip after a while. Aluminium and stainless steel pans can be lined with a non-stick

Caterers use a wide range of large pans, each specially designed for a particular cooking process.

coating of polytetrafluoroethylene (PTFE), which is a plastic that resists food deposits sticking to the surface. PTFE melts at a very high temperature, and is not damaged by the heat of cooking. The surface can be damaged by scratching, however, so only wooden or plastic (not metal) spoons should be used. Scouring pads and abrasive cleansers should not be used on them.

All pans should have the following features:

- ☐ a relatively thick base and sides for strength and durability
- ☐ a stable design that will not tip over easily
- ☐ handles made of an insulating material
- ☐ a lid that fits well and is easy to remove
- ☐ a flat base that has good contact with the hot plate
- ☐ well-fitting handles that do not become loose.

Kitchen knives

All kitchen knives should have a strong, easy-to-grip handle, a well-made blade that can be resharpened and retains its sharpness well and is rigid so that it does not bend when cutting (except palette knives which should be flexible).

Serrated knives have fine sharp points running along the blade. They remain sharp for a long time and are used to slice fruit and vegetables finely.

All sharp knives should be stored with the blades pointing downwards in a drawer or in a special rack. They should always be used on a chopping board, cutting away from the body.

Caterers use colour-coded knives to ensure different knives are used for each type of food product. This helps to prevent cross-contamination of bacteria which could cause food poisoning.

1 List three features of a well designed and made:
   a) electric food mixer
   b) food processor.

2 List four types of attachments that are available for:
   a) electric mixers
   b) food processors.

3 List four types of pan and what they can be used for.

4 What are the advantages and disadvantages of the following materials when considering the purchase of a set of pans:
   a) stainless steel
   b) aluminium
   c) PTFE?

5 List four features of a well designed pan.

6 What are the features of a well designed kitchen knife?

7 Give reasons why the following general features are important when choosing any piece of kitchen equipment (give examples):
   a) ease of cleaning   b) safety features   c) capacity
   d) durability   e) price.

4.13 MOIST METHODS OF COOKING (1)

BY THE END OF THIS SECTION, YOU SHOULD BE ABLE TO:

- identify the different moist methods of cooking and state which methods are most appropriate to different kinds of food
- understand the effects of moist cooking on the nutrient content of food

Moist methods of cooking apply heat to food through the medium of liquid. Relatively low temperatures are used and the liquid medium may be water, steam, stock, milk, fruit juice, wine or beer.

Boiling

Boiling is a common method of cooking. The liquid (usually water) is heated to boiling point and the heat is then lowered until the liquid is bubbling evenly and rapidly. It can be used to cook vegetables, tough cuts of meat, eggs, pasta and rice.

When boiling, the heat can be lowered to allow the food to simmer gently.

Foods that are cooked in hot water but require gentler treatment than boiling to prevent toughening (e.g. fish, meat), or to prevent the food breaking up (e.g. potatoes) should be **simmered**. When a liquid is simmering, few bubbles rise to the surface, and the temperature is just below boiling point.

Poaching

Poaching is the cooking of food in water at just below the temperature used for simmering. It is therefore a very gentle method of cooking.

The water should only come half way up the food, and the heat should be applied slowly until the right temperature is reached. This method is suitable for cooking foods containing protein which would become tough or curdled at higher temperatures, e.g. eggs, fish.

Poaching is an ideal way of cooking fish.

Rich puddings can be cooked by steaming.

Steaming

Food that is steamed does not come into direct contact with the water, but is cooked in the steam rising from boiling water. Steaming is suitable for cooking vegetables, fish and puddings. Food can be steamed in a variety of ways including: **plate method**, e.g. for fish, **saucepan method**, e.g. for puddings, **tiered steamer**, e.g. for cooking a whole meal, **stepped steamer**, e.g. for puddings of different sizes.

| Plate method | Tiered steamer | Stepped steamer |

Steaming is a versatile, economic and healthy method of cooking.

Pressure cookery

At normal atmospheric pressure, water boils at 100°C, but if the pressure is increased, the water will boil at a higher temperature. This forces very hot steam through food so that it cooks more rapidly and saves energy. A pressure cooker is suitable for jam-making, stews, vegetables, puddings and soups.

Most pressure cookers are made of aluminium, which is thicker

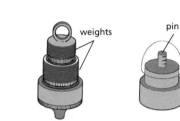

A pressure cooker showing the separate containers on the trivet inside. The separate containers enable different foods to be cooked at the same time. The trivet allows the steam to circulate under the food.

The pressure gauge on a pressure cooker can either have separate weights (left) or a pin which rises to indicate the pressure as it builds up (right).

than an ordinary pan. It is possible to buy stainless steel pressure cookers, but these tend to be more expensive. All pressure cookers have a pressure gauge, control valve, safety valve, locking lid, separate containers and a trivet.

Stewing

This is a slow method of cooking, which is similar to boiling, but the food is cooked below boiling point. It can be carried out on the hob in a pan with a lid, or in the oven in a covered dish (casserole) on a low heat (Gas 2–3, 150–160°C, 300–325°F). The liquid in which the food is cooked is served with the food. Stewing is suitable for meat, poultry and fruit.

1 Why is steaming a suitable method of cooking vegetables?

2 How do potatoes or rice become soft when boiled?

3 Why is it good practice to use the water in which vegetables have been boiled for making gravy or soup?

4 Why do pressure cookers cook food more quickly?

5 List three different moist methods of cooking.

6 Why is stewing a suitable method of cooking for tough cuts of meat?

Braising

Braising is a combination of stewing and roasting. Cuts of meat or poultry are placed on a bed of fried vegetables, bacon and herbs (a mirepoix) with sufficient liquid to cover the mirepoix and keep the food moist. A well-fitting lid is placed on the pan to prevent loss of liquid, while the food is cooking in the steam rising from the stock. When the food is tender, it is browned in a hot oven with the lid off. During cooking, the liquid should simmer, not boil, to avoid toughening the meat.

Industrial equipment used for moist cooking methods

Pans

In industrial and commercial kitchens, a variety of pans of different capacity (10 – 40 litres) are available for boiling, stewing, poaching and braising. They may be heated by an electric or gas supply, and many are fitted with a device to enable them to tilt, so that the contents can be safely poured out. Some have a double wall to prevent the food inside from being burned. Bratt pans have a large surface area, which enables a large quantity of food to be cooked at one time. They can also be used for shallow and deep frying.

Steamers

Industrial steaming ovens are used for a variety of cooking methods including steaming, poaching, stewing, braising, and blanching. Some models cook the food under pressure, and many combine a variety of methods, e.g. hot air cooking, convection steaming.

Slow cookers

Slow cookers are operated by electricity and can be used for cooking stews, braises and other dishes that require long, slow, moist cooking. They can also be used to cook pâtés, soups, fish and desserts.

There are several types available, but they all have the same basic design with a metal or plastic case into which an earthenware or stoneware pot is fitted. The heating element is located under the base or around the sides of the pot. There is no thermostat to control the temperature as very little power is used to operate them. Food can be left to cook for up to 14 hours. Some models also have two heat settings.

As the build-up of heat is slow, some models have to be pre-heated for about 20 minutes before food is placed in them. This avoids the risk of food-poisoning bacteria multiplying as the food warms up. Red kidneys beans should be boiled separately and added before serving, as the temperature in the slow cooker may not be high enough to destroy the natural toxin in the beans.

Tough cuts of meat can be tenderized in a slow cooker.

Comparison of moist methods of cooking

Method	Advantages	Disadvantages
Boiling	The transfer of heat by convection is fairly rapid and efficient and water is readily available, food is unlikely to burn, though it may disintegrate if overcooked.	Nutrient loss may be high, soluble matter may be lost into the liquid and some flavour is lost from meat. The disadvantages can be partly overcome by serving the cooking water as gravy, sauce, or stock with the meal.
Poaching	Cooks protein gently avoiding toughness or curdling developing	Food requires careful preparation and handling. Longer cooking time.
Steaming	Loss of nutrients is reduced as the food does not come into direct contact with the water. Food cooked in this way is easy to digest and has a light texture. The food is unlikely to be overcooked.	Food takes a long time to cook, so the heat destruction of vitamin C is more likely to occur.
Pressure cookery	Pressure cookers are economical on fuel. Meals can be prepared quickly. Nutrient loss by leaching is reduced, though heat destruction still occurs. Whole meals can be cooked in one pan. Tough cuts of meat can be cooked quickly and tenderized.	
Slow cookers	Once the cooking starts the pot can be left unattended, except for rice dishes which should be stirred occasionally. Tough cuts of meat can be tenderized by the slow cooking. Little fuel is used.	Pulses and beans may not cook completely at the temperature of the slow cooker. Red kidney beans should be boiled for 10 minutes beforehand to destroy the toxin they contain.
Stewing	Stewing tenderizes tough cuts of meat, and nutrient losses are kept to a minimum. The flavour is retained as the liquid is served with the meal. Stewing improves certain fruits (e.g. plums, rhubarb) as the cellulose is softened. The fruit acids help to keep vitamin C and thiamin losses to a minimum. A whole meal can be prepared in one container, which saves time and clearing up. A large variety of stews and casseroles can be prepared	Stewing is a long, slow method of cooking, and there is little variation in texture and consistency. It is relatively economical.
Braising	A whole meal can be cooked in one pan, saving time and fuel. Tough cuts of meat can be used.	Meat may not develop a good colour and may need to be grilled at the end of cooking.

1 What are the advantages of slow cookers to:
   a) people who work long hours
   b) people on low incomes
   c) people with limited cooking facilities?

2 What safety precautions should be taken when cooking:
   a) red kidney beans in a slow cooker
   b) soup in a pressure cooker
   c) a steamed pudding?

3 What effects do moist methods of cooking have on water-soluble vitamins?

BY THE END OF THIS SECTION, YOU SHOULD BE ABLE TO:

- identify the different dry methods of cooking and state which methods are most appropriate for different kinds of food
- understand the effects of dry cooking on the nutrient content of food

In dry methods of cooking, heat is applied directly to food. High temperatures are used.

Baking

Baking is cooking by **convection** in an oven, i.e. heat is transferred by the movement of air from cool regions to warmer regions of lower density. It can be used to cook cakes, biscuits, pastries, bread, fruit and vegetables.

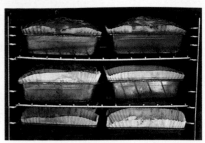
Baking is ideal for cakes, breads and pastries.

Roasting

Roasting is the cooking of meat or vegetables such as potatoes or parsnips in the oven, basting them with hot fat to prevent drying and to develop colour and flavour.

There are three main methods of roasting meat.

Searing

The meat is put into a very hot oven (Gas 8–9, 230–240°C, 450–470°F) for the first 20 minutes to sear (heat-seal) the outside and develop the flavour and extractives. The heat is then lowered to complete the cooking. This method is only suitable for tender joints of meat, e.g. topside of beef, leg of lamb or pork, and care should be taken not to overharden the meat.

Slow roasting

Meat is baked at a cool temperature (Gas 3, 170°C, 325°F) for double the usual time, resulting in a tender joint which does not, however, develop such a full flavour. This method is suitable for cuts such as breast of lamb, belly of pork, or brisket of beef.

Cold oven method

The meat is put into a cold oven, set at Gas 7, 220°C (425°F), and the gradual rise in temperature tenderizes the meat and develops the flavour. Any cuts of meat can be cooked by this method, but it is particularly suitable for the less tender cuts, e.g. shoulder of lamb, brisket of beef.

Roasting is suitable for large joints of meat.

Grilling

Grilling is the cooking of food by radiation under a gas or electric grill. The surface of the food is quickly sealed, and the flavour is well developed. The food must be moistened with fat to prevent it from drying out and turned frequently to ensure even cooking. The food to be grilled should not be more than 2.5–3.5 cm thick, to allow heat penetration. The use of skewers or bones in meat joints helps heat penetration by conduction.

Small items such as chops, bacon, sausages and tomatoes can be cooked quite quickly by grilling.

Grilling is suitable for cooking tender meat cuts, sausages, burgers, offal, fish fillets and tomatoes. It can also be used to brown foods such as cheese, potatoes, sauces, and crumpets, and to toast bread.

Comparison of dry methods of cooking		
Cooking method	Advantages	Disadvantages
Baking	Several items can be baked at the same time. Baking is ideal for delicate food e.g. pastry, meringue, sponge cake.	The oven has to be preheated. Baking requires careful timing. If the oven is opened too soon, heat is lost and the food may spoil.
Roasting	Roasting tenderizes joints of meat and develops their flavour. Little attention is required while the meat is roasting, except to baste the joint. Fuel can be saved if other items are baked in the oven at the same time.	A lot of moisture is lost by evaporation and the joint may dry out. Meat may shrink markedly as a result of moisture loss and protein denaturation. High temperatures may result in toughening of protein and reduced digestibility. Fat from the meat will spatter at high temperatures, making the oven dirty.
Grilling	Grilling is a quick method of cooking and is therefore suitable for snacks, and for time-saving meals. It is a healthy method of cooking because the fat from the meat, bacon, etc., drains away.	Grilling requires careful timing to prevent overcooking. Meat to be grilled must be tender and will therefore be more expensive.

1 List two dry methods of cooking.

2 Why do fan ovens give a more even heat than ordinary ovens?

3 Why does roasted meat become tough and indigestible if overheated?

4 How does grilling transfer heat to cook food?

5 Why is grilling a more healthy method of cooking than frying?

6 Why do foods such as bread and biscuits develop a brown crust when baked?

7 Why might a fan oven be more useful than an ordinary oven to a batch production company (such as Cilla's Homemade Cakes – see Section 5.4)?

8 Why do many microwave oven manufacturers include features such as grills and convection ovens in their range of models?

5.1 PRODUCTION SYSTEMS

BY THE END OF THIS SECTION, YOU SHOULD BE ABLE TO:

- understand what a system is
- identify, explain and give examples of the parts of a system

A **system** is a set of things, operations or parts which are connected together to work as a whole for a specific purpose. For example, the digestive system in the body consists of a variety of organs and tubes connected to each other for the specific purpose of breaking down food, removing nutrients and disposing of waste.

Food production systems, like all systems, have three basic elements:

- **Input** is everything that goes into a system. In the case of food production, this would include the ingredients, the specification, packaging materials and energy.
- **Process** is what happens to the input to make a product.
- **Output** is the finished product, any wastage or by-product materials for recycling.

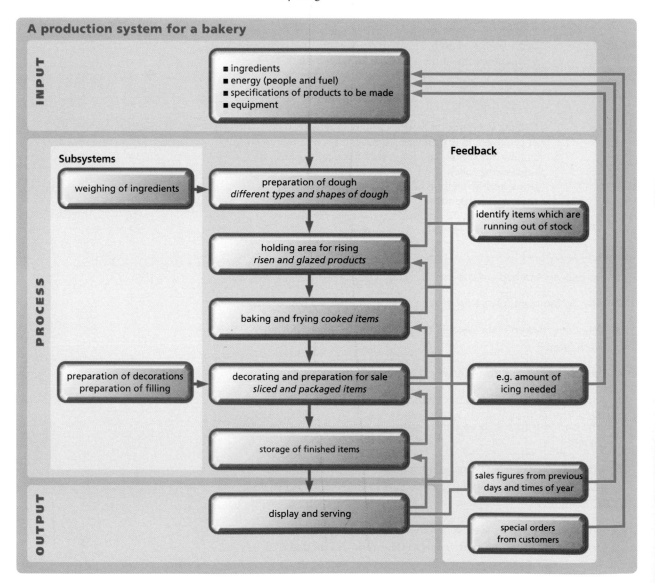

A system may be broken down into **sub-systems** to make sure it is as efficient and streamlined as possible. Each sub-system will have its own output, which becomes the input to the next sub-system. The whole system needs to be controlled so information from one sub-system is passed back to another. This is called **feedback**.

For example, in a small independent bakery, producing bread and sweet yeast dough products such as buns and doughnuts, there would need to be feedback about the number of loaves being sold daily, so that the right amounts of ingredients could be made available to make sufficient dough for the day's requirements.

In this bakery, a variety of products are at different stages of production to ensure a continuous supply of freshly baked goods.

In a large production system, the whole operation may be analysed in order to decide how a computer could be used to operate and control it. This is called **systems analysis**, and is often used to reduce operating and production costs. More information about computer control is given in Section 5.3.

---

1 What are the three basic elements in a system?

2 What information may be given as feedback in the following systems:
   a) digestive biscuit production
   b) take-away kebab production
   c) cook-chill chicken curry dinner production?

3 Write down a system for the production of:
   a) take-away fish and chips
   b) ploughman's lunches at a school fundraising event
   c) a midday meal for 20 patients on a hospital ward.

In any production system, good planning is essential to ensure that **resources** (i.e. time, money, equipment, materials and human labour) are used efficiently and effectively. This will ensure that the end product meets the needs, specifications and requirements set out in the design process, and is successful, i.e. makes a profit and continues to be purchased.

Whatever the size or type of organization involved in food production, it is important that a **production schedule** is prepared for all products. This should show the following:

- ☐ purchase of materials and components
- ☐ storage of materials and components
- ☐ start of production
- ☐ workforce and equipment to be used at various stages of production
- ☐ end of production
- ☐ storage
- ☐ despatch and delivery of product.

Depending on the size and type of organization, various managers will be employed to ensure that the schedule runs smoothly and that resources are managed efficiently. In the case of a small organization, one person may well be responsible for everything!

The buyer

The function of the buyer is to identify quality materials and reliable suppliers, and to purchase materials and components (goods) at competitive prices. He or she must have a good knowledge of materials, components, production processes and the needs of the company they work for.

The production manager

The production manager is responsible for all stages of the production process and supervises staff on the production line. He or she must ensure that the right amount and type of products are produced to meet the orders, on time.

Checking the stock in the warehouse.

The warehouse and stock controller

The warehouse and stock controller controls goods in and out of the warehouse and stock. He or she is responsible for organizing the stock so that goods and end products are tidy, stored correctly to keep them in good condition, and can be easily located and identified (e.g. colour-coded). Another task is to rotate stock to prevent wastage due to overlooking use-by dates. He or she must have a good knowledge of materials used and end products.

Personnel manager

The job of the personnel manager is to organize the workforce to carry out specific tasks without wasting their time and energy moving unnecessarily from one place to another, to identify people who can carry out a task most effectively and to train the workforce to improve efficiency, skill and output. The personnel manager should ensure that the workforce is properly looked after, happy in their work and that health and safety regulations are observed.

Equipment manager

The equipment manager organizes the use and maintenance of equipment, and ensures that high standards of hygiene and safety are maintained and that the workforce is provided with the right tools and equipment to carry out their tasks. He or she must have a good knowledge of production processes.

Distribution manager

The role of the distribution manager is to ensure that orders are met and delivered on time. He or she must be able to adapt to changing demands for products, e.g. more ice-cream orders in hot weather, and must be able to deal with problems and complaints from customers.

A refrigerated van for delivering food.

1 What is a production schedule, and what should it show?

2 Why does a warehouse and stock controller need to have good knowledge of the food components and products he or she deals with?

3 Why are the following important for efficient food production:
   a) keeping tools (e.g. knives) sharp
   b) regular maintenance of equipment on a production line
   c) regular training of staff
   d) a tidy workplace
   e) careful, logical recording and filing of orders, payments and receipts
   f) good customer relations?

5.2 ORGANIZING A FOOD PRODUCTION SYSTEM (2)

BY THE END OF THIS SPREAD, YOU SHOULD BE ABLE TO:

■ recognize the benefits of using flow charts when organizing food production

Flow charts

In efficient food production, food should be processed from the point where it is delivered to the point where it is distributed or sold with the minimum amount of obstruction. To help achieve this, **flow charts** can be produced. These should show that:

☐ the various processes are separated

☐ there are no wasteful movements and journeys by the workforce

☐ refuse and waste foods are kept well away from food production

☐ maximum use is made of space and equipment.

The flow chart should be shown to and followed by the workforce in every stage of the production process.

A flow chart for the production of salads might look like the one at left or, for the preparation and sale of fish and chips, like the one below.

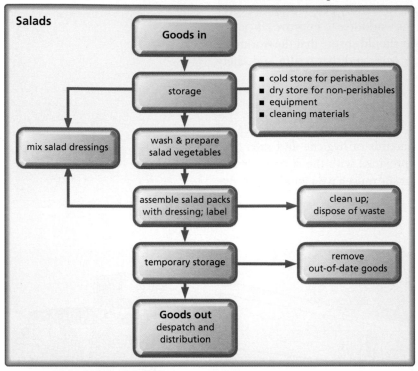

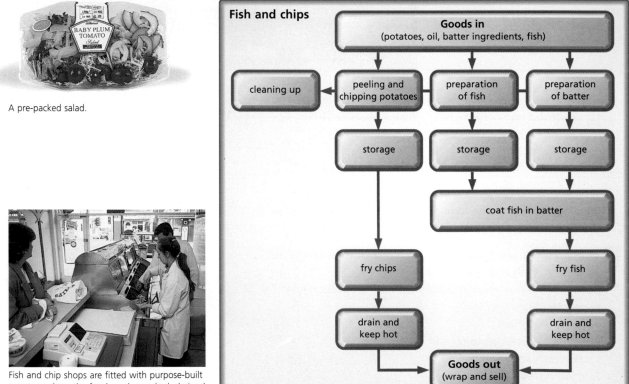

A pre-packed salad.

Fish and chip shops are fitted with purpose-built counters where the food can be cooked, drained and held in a hot cabinet ready for serving.

For a restaurant kitchen the flow chart might look like this:

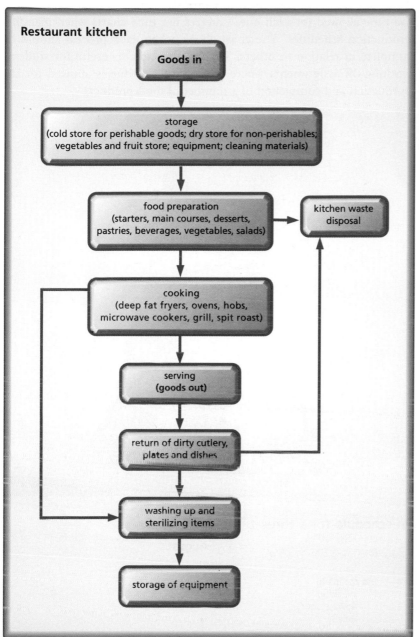

Restaurant kitchen

```
Goods in
   │
   ▼
storage
(cold store for perishable goods; dry store for non-perishables;
vegetables and fruit store; equipment; cleaning materials)
   │
   ▼
food preparation                    kitchen waste
(starters, main courses, desserts, ───►  disposal
pastries, beverages, vegetables, salads)
   │
   ▼
cooking
(deep fat fryers, ovens, hobs,
microwave cookers, grill, spit roast)
   │
   ▼
serving
(goods out)
   │
   ▼
return of dirty cutlery,
plates and dishes
   │
   ▼
washing up and
sterilizing items
   │
   ▼
storage of equipment
```

Preparing vegetables in a restaurant kitchen.

1 Make a flow chart for the following:
  a) the production of hot dogs and burgers (cooked on a barbecue)
     at a school function
  b) the production of self-service breakfasts in a hotel kitchen.

2 Make a flow chart for the following:
  a) the production and delivery of meals on wheels
  b) the production and serving of school meals (cafeteria system).

Time charts

Time charts list the order in which processes should be carried out, and the time allowed for each one. Caterers use time charts when planning production schedules. The chart shows when each process should be complete in relation to others. Time charts are also useful for students working on assignments where only a limited time is allowed for the production and completion of a number of food products.

Large wedding cakes are prepared in stages over several months as the rich fruit cake needs time to mature and the marzipan and icing need time to dry out.

Production schedule for a three-tier wedding cake

June	July	August	
■ bake cakes	■ start preparation of petals for sugar flowers	■ complete individual flowers and leaves	
■ wrap and store to allow them to mature	■ make sugar leaves	■ marzipan cakes	■ flat ice cakes
			■ add piping and decoration
			■ make flowers and leaves into sprays
			■ assemble cake with pillars and flower sprays
			■ deliver

A time chart for an assignment to prepare vegetable soup, bread rolls and fruit salad in one hour could look like this:

Assignment plan for a lunch menu

Time	Process	Notes
9.00	Light oven.	225°C/Gas 7
9.01	Sieve flour, salt, dried yeast and crushed vitamin C tablet. Add warm water, mix and knead for 5 minutes.	Fast-acting yeast used (no need to activate first).
9.08	Shape into rolls, and leave in warm place to rise for 30 minutes.	Cover with oiled plastic bag to prevent drying out.
9.15	Wash up and clear away.	
9.20	Wash, peel and chop vegetables.	
9.25	Place in pan and sauté in oil for 5 minutes. Boil water in kettle.	
9.30	Add stock cube and water to pan. Simmer soup for 20 minutes.	Stir occasionally.
9.32	Wash up and clear away.	
9.37	Wash, peel and chop fruit. Add fruit juice and chill.	Prepare fruits that brown last.
9.45	Glaze rolls with egg. Place in oven for 10–12 minutes.	Should be well risen, golden, and sound hollow when tapped after baking.
9.50	Check soup vegetables are tender. Liquidize soup, pour into dish, keep hot.	Taste, and adjust seasoning if necessary.
9.58	Remove rolls and serve.	
9.59	Garnish soup and serve. Serve fruit salad.	
10.00	Do final clearing up.	

Even a simple meal requires careful advance planning if all the items are to be freshly prepared and served on time.

1 Why are time charts useful to: a) someone planning the production schedule for a three-course meal for a wedding reception
b) a student carrying out a practical food assignment
c) a busy hotel kitchen?

2 Write out a time chart for the production of stir-fried chicken and vegetables, brown rice, and peach sponge flan in one hour, starting at 10 am.

5.3 CONTROLLING A FOOD PRODUCTION SYSTEM

BY THE END OF THIS SECTION, YOU SHOULD BE ABLE TO:

- understand the importance of controlling a system
- understand the importance of feedback in a system
- identify ways of controlling large and small scale food production systems

Chocolate coating must be of uniform consistency and thickness.

Control and feedback are important in a food production system because they:

- help to ensure that production meets consumer demand for products (i.e. so that neither too much nor too little is made)
- ensure that products are of a consistent quality (always the same so that consumers know what to expect)
- enable production to run efficiently (so that time, energy and materials are not wasted and production schedules are met)
- enable any faults to be detected (e.g. the wrong temperature, a foreign body in the food, blockages, incorrect filling of containers)
- enable food regulations to be followed during preparation to make sure that the food sold is safe.

Large scale systems

In large scale food production, control is often carried out by computers. This is often called Computer-Aided Manufacture or CAM. Information from all stages of a food production system is collected by electronic sensors, which are designed to detect any changes in the food. For example, weight changes in containers are detected by sensors called load cells, pieces of metal which accidentally find their way into food are found by metal detectors, and temperature changes inside equipment such as ovens and freezing units are detected and controlled by thermocouples. Other changes in food that can be detected by sensors include:

- change in colour as a product is cooked
- the thickness of a product, e.g. pastry
- the change in the properties of fish skin as the fish deteriorate.

The information is sent back to a central unit to be interpreted. The central unit then sends instructions back to other parts of the system based on this information, and they respond accordingly. Information which is sent back to be acted upon is called feedback.

Food retail

Computer control is also used by many of the large retail companies (shops and supermarkets) to give them very detailed information about sales of food. By monitoring which products sell the most and least, at what times of day they sell most and least and the effect of changes in the weather on sales, retailers are able to organize efficient stock rotation, ordering and stocktaking.

Milk production lines are monitored constantly.

Bar codes are printed on every packaged product, and each type has a different code which is recognized by the store's computer. Each product is scanned at the check-out, and appears on the customer receipt with a brief description, its weight/size and its price so that it can be checked if required. Bar codes are also used on packing cases to allow monitoring of products as they move through the chain of production, storage, distribution and retail.

Some retailers use computerized control of their chill cabinets, refrigerators and freezers, which ensures they are complying with legislation about safe temperatures for storing foods.

The bar code on food packaging is scanned at the till which displays the name and price of the product.

Small scale systems

In small scale food production, control is carried out by people rather than machines or computers. They have to use their skills to carry out a variety of processes in a consistent way, for example:

☐ selecting, measuring and preparing ingredients
☐ combining and mixing ingredients
☐ heating and cooling food to the correct temperatures and for the required length of time
☐ flavouring, colouring, cooking and serving foods to consumer requirements.

Specialised equipment helps with production control. For example:

☐ food processors and mixers process and mix ingredients for a set time and speed
☐ scales and measuring cups or spoons ensure that the same quantity of ingredients is used each time
☐ baking tins of set sizes and shapes give the same sized product each time
☐ timers ensure that the same cooking time is used for identical products
☐ thermostats and temperature probes are used to ensure that food is heated to the correct temperature.

1 Give four reasons why control in a food production system is important.

2 In a system of food production that uses CAM, what information might sensors detect and feed back to a central unit in the following:
   a) canned chicken soup production and packaging
   b) breakfast cereal packaging
   c) jam tart production and packaging
   d) ice-cream production and packaging?

3 How do bar codes benefit retailers and consumers?

4 How have changes in food production affected the numbers of people employed in the industry?

5.4 BATCH PRODUCTION

By the end of this section, you should be able to:

- appreciate the amount of time and energy required to run a company which operates a batch production system
- understand the advantages and disadvantages of this type of production

Cilla's Homemade Butter Shortbread
Ingredients:
Butter, Flour and Sugar

Cilla's Homemade Tangy Lemon Slices
Ingredients:
Fresh Eggs, Fresh Lemons

Cilla's Homemade Chocolate Victoria
Ingredients:
Margarine, Sugar, Fresh Eggs and Cocoa Powder
Margarine, Icing Sugar and Vanilla Essence

Cilla's Homemade Jam Filled Victoria
Ingredients:
Flour, Soft Margarine, Sugar, Fresh Eggs and Jam

A simple system of labelling and packaging helps to keep production costs down.

When more than one type of product is required, each product can be made in **batches** of a convenient quantity. One or more people may be involved in producing and assembling the different parts of such products. Batch production is often used to make products such as pies; specialized breads, cakes and pastries; hand-made chocolates; specialized cooked meats, sausages, cheeses and pâtés; salads; specialized smoked meats, including game and fish.

The quantities involved in batch production are usually much less than those in mass production. *Cilla's Homemade Cakes* in Crowborough, East Sussex, is a batch production company owned by Cilla Piper. It supplies a selected number of local village shops, restaurants and coffee shops, and has a steady demand all year round for its products. A range of 25 different products are made from three basic categories of cake: small cakes and slices, loaf cakes and sponge cakes.

Organizing the production

Cakes which need finishing off by icing or cutting into slices are made first each day, e.g. flapjacks, almond slices, Viennese slices, apple cake. Cakes which do not need any finishing are baked while the first batches are being finished, e.g. ginger cake, family fruit cake, banana and walnut loaf cake. Cilla only prepares as much of any mixture as can be baked at one time, as the quality of uncooked mixture will spoil if it is left standing.

Production for each week is organized as follows:

- ☐ Monday: replacement of stock for shops – there must be enough packaged products in stock to meet demand, e.g. loaf cakes are made in batches of eight and at the end of the day there must be 16 cakes of each type in stock
- ☐ Tuesday: production of items for restaurants and coffee shops
- ☐ Wednesday: delivery of products to shops
- ☐ Thursday: production of cakes for restaurants and shops
- ☐ Friday: delivery of products to restaurants and coffee shops; cleaning of kitchen and storage areas; deliveries of ingredients received from wholesalers.

Quality control

Set recipes and quantities of ingredients are used for each product. There could be a problem if the wholesaler changes their supplier, and the quality of the ingredient changes as a result.

The size of the products which are baked in cake tins is controlled by filling the container to the same level each time. The size of other items, e.g. Viennese fingers which are piped by hand, is controlled by visual comparison. Consistency of mixtures is controlled by using an electric mixer at the same speed for a set length of time.

Supply of products

Customers have their orders delivered to them. Restaurants have their products supplied in large plastic cake boxes, which are then kept in their stock rooms. Shops have their products packaged and labelled, and normally telephone their requirements to Cilla when their stocks are running low. Cilla produces her own printed labels, and uses the minimum amount of simple packaging in order to keep costs down. Different customers who order the same products as each other are encouraged to have them cut or packaged in the same way, e.g. slices cut to the same size and shape, to make production easy to control.

In a small bakery, biscuits may be piped by hand, leading to a slight variation in the size of the products.

Feedback and quality assurance

Cilla receives feedback from both restaurant and shop proprietors about consumer reaction to her products, both positive and negative. Refunds are given if a product is faulty.

Product development

When Cilla develops a new product, all customers are sent samples on a **sale or return** basis (they can send back what they don't sell) to gain feedback and to encourage them to place orders.

Overheads

Overheads are the items that any business must pay for before it can start making a profit. In Cilla's family business overheads include ingredients, packaging materials, fuel and water bills, replacement of equipment, cleaning materials, petrol and other car expenses, and the cost of damaged and unsold items returned by customers. In a larger business there would also be wages to take into account, if full-time or part-time production or cleaning staff are employed.

---

1 Give three examples of groups of products made by this system.

2 Why do batch production companies tend to be small, often family businesses?

3 What are 'overheads'? Give examples of the overheads the batch production companies producing the following might have:
a) specialist cheeses b) pies and tarts c) picnic hampers.

4 What does a small company using this type of system need to do in order to establish and maintain good customer relations, good quality and a profitable business?

5 Find out which main legal requirements such a company would have to comply with.

5.5 ASSEMBLY LINE PRODUCTION

When very large numbers of one product are required, e.g. biscuits, confectionery, cakes, snack foods and frozen foods, they can be **mass-produced** in a **flow line** or **assembly line** system. Producing goods quickly and effeciently in large numbers keeps the unit cost of each item low.

Purpose-built machinery is used for as many processes as possible, e.g. peeling, mixing, rolling out, cutting out shapes, moulding shapes, filling, decorating and packaging. The product is usually passed from one process to another on a **conveyor belt**.

Large numbers of people are often employed on the **production line** to operate machinery, pack finished products or carry out tasks for which there is no machinery available, e.g. decorating, filleting and boning. Such repetitive skills can be learned quickly, but may lead to operators becoming bored and fatigued.

In assembly line production goods pass from one operator to the next on a conveyor belt to keep up a steady flow of production.

The production process needs to be well organized and maintained to avoid breakdowns and hold-ups as low production rates mean higher unit costs for each item. However, once the assembly line has been set up and is running efficiently, the running costs should be relatively low, enabling products to be sold at competitive prices.

Quality control on assembly lines can be very straightforward, which enables the manufacturer to give quality assurance to customers, who will in turn have confidence about the product and buy it repeatedly. Many companies use computers to control production and operate machinery, thus reducing the number of people they need to employ.

The potatoes are loaded into the slicing machine.

Manufacturing potato crisps

Potato crisps are produced on an assembly line system. Potato crisps have two main components – potatoes and vegetable oil. The three main types of oil used are palm oil (from Malaysia), rape seed oil (from Europe) and soya oil (from the USA).

Primary processing

After quality checks on the crop, potatoes are taken from the field to purpose-built stores where they are kept in carefully controlled conditions.

Secondary processing

At the crisp factory, the potatoes are graded and washed. They are then peeled mechanically and after visual inspection moved on to the slicer where they are cut into slices on average 1.27 mm thick. To keep them sharp, the blades in the slicing machine have to be changed frequently to ensure thickness consistency.

The slices are washed again to remove surface starch before frying. They are cooked in oil at around 185°C for three to four minutes. During the continuous frying operation, fresh oil is continually being added.

The crisps pass along a conveyor where surface oil is drained off and they receive a further visual quality inspection.

Next the crisps are dusted with salt and flavourings, and are tumbled in a rotating drum to ensure these are spread evenly.

After frying the crisps are inspected by operators who pick out and discard any that are sub-standard.

Packaging

The crisps are transported by conveyor to multi-head weighers which control the amount of crisps going in to each packet. The packets are formed from a reel of packaging film with a 'best before' date stamped on each packet. They are filled at a rate of more than one packet per second. The packets are then put in cardboard boxes or multipack bags before being delivered to the retail outlets.

The crisps from this company are packed and despatched immediately to ensure maximum freshness.

1 What does 'mass-produced' mean?

2 List eight types of food products that are mass-produced.

3 Why does this type of system need to be well organized?

4 How can the managers of such a system ensure that the people who work for them do not become bored and fatigued with repetitive jobs?

5 What are the main costs in setting up such a system?

6 What problems might arise outside of the system which could result in hold-ups and breakdowns? How might such problems be solved?

5.6 CONTINUOUS PROCESS PRODUCTION

BY THE END OF THIS SECTION, YOU SHOULD BE ABLE TO:

- identify examples of products made in this type of system
- understand the need for good organization and maintenance in such a system
- understand the advantages and disadvantages of this type of system

Certain products for which there is a high demand, e.g. soft drinks, refined sugar, and fats and oils, are manufactured from raw materials by a **continuous process**, often for 24 hours a day, seven days a week.

This is also known as a **continual flow process**. Expensive machinery, very often computer-controlled, is used to produce a high quality, consistent product. Usually the reason for continuous production is that it would be difficult to close down production and re-start it again without it costing a lot of money. This also means that the machinery must be regularly maintained, to avoid expensive breakdowns and loss of production.

Once set up, continuous production is relatively cheap to run, and as few people are required to operate machinery, employment costs are low.

Manufacturing fats

Margarine, vegetable fat and spread manufacture is a large industry. Since the process of converting liquid oils to solid fats by hydrogenation was developed, large numbers of new products have been introduced and are produced in enormous quantities. Hydrogenation is a good example of continuous process production.

Unhardened oil goes in at the start of the process and is mixed with a **catalyst** (usually nickel) which speeds up the process of hydrogenation. Hydrogen gas is added under pressure, and the hardened oil is filtered to remove the catalyst, then removed at the end of the system.

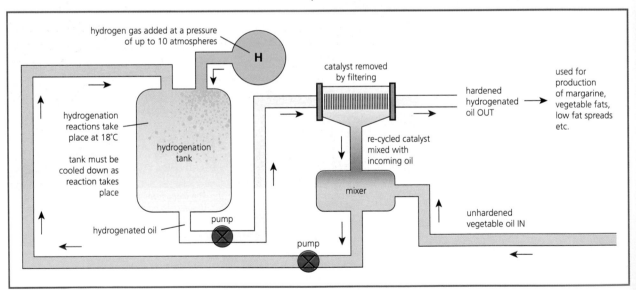

The hydrogenation process.

1 Why is this system different from assembly line systems where items are mass-produced?

2 Why is the production continuous?

3 Why is the production usually relatively cheap to run?

5.7 ONE-OFF OR CRAFT PRODUCTION

END OF THIS SECTION, YOU SHOULD BE ABLE TO:

- identify the types of product made in this type of system
- understand what the term 'specialist' means
- identify the advantages and disadvantages of this type of production

One-off or **craft production** (also known as **job production**) is used when a customer orders one product to meet their own requirements e.g. a celebration iced cake for a wedding, a giant Easter egg for a charity, or a giant pie for a competition.

The order is placed with a specialist who is very experienced at making such a product. Several weeks notice may be required, so the customer must plan ahead.

The price will include a fee for the specialists's expertise and time spent in making the product, but the finished product will be unique.

Creative Cakecraft in Crowborough, East Sussex, is owned by Maria Bennewith who specializes in the production of cakes for any celebration, as well as selling cake icing and decorating materials, and teaching sugarcraft courses.

Assembling the pre-prepared decorations on a celebration cake.

A wide range of equipment and trimmings have to be kept in stock to suit the requirements of individual customers.

Photographs of previous cakes help customers select a design, as well as promoting the business.

When placing an order, the customer and supplier agree a specification and price and the details are written down. The customer pays a deposit for the cost of the cake to indicate their commitment to buying the finished product.

Fruit cakes are baked to order, three to six weeks in advance. Some cakes are baked and kept in stock for last minute orders. The cakes are then covered with almond paste (**marzipan**) four to six weeks before they are flat-iced. Decorations such as sugar flowers, leaves, models and decorated plaques are made to order and stored until the cake is assembled.

A wedding cake is usually decorated about two weeks before the date required. Sponge cakes are made three days in advance and decorated the day before they are required.

Customers usually collect the finished product from the shop, but wedding cakes are often delivered and set up for the wedding reception by the supplier. This ensures safe delivery and correct assembly of the cake, which is especially important for tiered cakes and those with delicate sugar flower arrangements.

1 Why do one-off products tend to cost more than similar mass-produced products?

2 Give reasons why a consumer may place an order for a product with a specialist.

3 How should a specialist, such as a cake maker and decorator, organize their business so that it is run efficiently and provides a good and profitable service for customers?

6.1 PRODUCT ANALYSIS (1)

BY THE END OF THIS SECTION, YOU SHOULD BE ABLE TO:

- understand the importance of product analysis in the development of new food products
- understand what is meant by sensory analysis

To analyse something means to examine it closely in order to understand how it works, what it is made of, the effect it has on other things and how it could be improved. For example you could analyse a food product, a production system or an unknown substance.

An **analysis** is usually a written statement about what has been analysed. It might include:

- a list of attributes, e.g. texture, flavour, colour and shape, of a product
- data (facts), e.g. volume, size, weight, nutritional profile and components
- observations, i.e. what the analyst (the person doing the analysis) sees, hears, feels, tastes and smells
- survey or test results
- conclusions and suggestions.

Product analysis

Product analysis can be carried out on both new and existing food products from the same or rival manufacturers in order to find out:

- how suitable a product is for its **intended market** (or **target group**) i.e. the group of people that the product development team consider most likely to buy the product
- why the product is presented to consumers in a particular way, e.g. uncooked or ready to eat
- why certain materials and components have been used in the product
- why certain processes have been carried out on the product
- how the product compares to alternative similar products already available in terms of quality, cost, flavour, image.

Sensory analysis

Sensory analysis of food products is used to find out, measure and decide on the **sensory qualities** – flavour, texture, appearance, smell or sound. It is used by the food industry to develop new products, improve existing products and change an existing product to keep it in line with dietary guidelines (e.g. reducing salt content) without noticeably changing the eating quality.

Sensory analysis is also used to assess the shelf-life of products and carry out quality control (see Section 7.1). Analysis will also show whether or not using a new ingredient or changing a production process affects the sensory qualities of a product. Manufacturers may need to compare a product with that of a competitor, to establish whether or not it is the sensory qualities or other factors, such as image, advertising or packaging, which will affect the sales figures.

Sensory analysis uses a series of scientifically designed and controlled tests so that the results are as accurate as possible (see Section 6.2). Trained testers are given samples of food products to look at, smell and/or taste, and, for some foods, to listen to. The testers produce their results in the form of **descriptors** (words that describe a characteristic of the product).

A tester checks a sample of cake for taste and texture.

Sensory descriptors			
Sensor organ	**Characteristic**	**Descriptor**	**Examples**
Eye	appearance	colour	golden brown, dull red, bright orange, light, dark
		texture/pattern	shiny, runny, curdled, speckled
Nose	smell	aroma/odour	burnt, acid, sour, putrid, flowery, spicy, yeasty, fruity
Skin	touch or	texture/ mouthfeel	soft, smooth, greasy, crunchy, tangy, fizzy, woody, juicy, sticky, chewy, tough, tender, lumpy, gritty
	temperature	hot/cold	hot, warm, cold, sizzling, blazing, smoking
Tongue	taste	flavour	sweet, salt, bitter, hot (spicy), mild, weak, strong, savoury, sharp
		food type	onion, lemon, coconut, chocolate, aniseed, peppermint, vinegar, garlic, meat, barbecue
Ear	sound	noise	crackling, fizzing, popping, crunchy, rustling

One way of checking cheese for ripeness is to take a core from it with a special tool and test it by smell.

Hedonic descriptors describe likes and dislikes, e.g. horrible, nice, delicious, foul, appetizing, lovely, quite good, revolting, repulsive, gorgeous.

Attitudinal descriptors describe what people feel about the product and beliefs and attitudes that the product evokes, e.g. healthy, relieves stress, gives energy, traditional, old-fashioned, satisfying, natural, artificial.

1 What does sensory analysis mean?

2 List three reasons why food manufacturers use sensory analysis.

3 What is a sensory descriptor? Give ten examples.

4 What is a hedonic descriptor? Give five examples.

5 List the attributes you might associate with:
a) potato crisps b) an eating apple c) a salad-filled bread roll.

6 Where would you find out data about a food product?

7 Give three reasons for carrying out a product analysis.

8 Select one food product from any of the following groups, and make an analysis of its attributes, data, sensory aspects (taste, smell, appearance, texture), presentation, suitability for its target group(s) (give reasons). Make a comparison with similar products:
a) low fat spreads b) 'live' (bio) yoghurt c) cereal-based sweet snack bars d) dips for party food e) dried soups f) vegetarian burgers.

Variables

When any food product is made, a number of **variables** (factors) that can be changed contribute to the final result. For example, in cake-making these include:

- amount and type of individual ingredients
- method and time of mixing
- method and time of cooking.

Each variable that can be changed is called an **independent variable (IV)**. In a test, one or more IVs can be altered, and the effect of that alteration on the resulting **dependent variables (DVs)** is measured. In the cake example, the DVs could be:

- colour of the finished product
- lightness/heaviness of texture
- dryness/moistness of cake
- volume of cake (how much it has risen).

A perfect Victoria sponge should have an even texture, be well risen and have a smooth, lightly browned top.

A cake which has sunk in the middle may contain too much sugar or raising agent, or it may be undercooked or else the oven door was opened too soon.

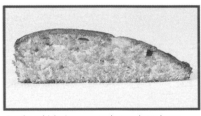

A cake which rises unevenly may have been baked in an oven with shelves that are not level, or it may have been placed at the side of the oven so that the heat caused the mixture to rise more quickly on one side.

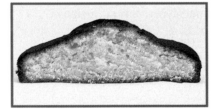

A cake which rises to a peak and is cracked and burnt has either been baked in too small a tin or placed on too high a shelf in the oven and baked at too high a temperature.

To achieve an accurate test result, all IVs *apart* from the one being altered, must be controlled and kept the same.

Sugar as a variable

When testing a plain cake recipe for example, the IV which might be altered could be the amount of sugar in the mixture (e.g. reducing it by 10%, then 25%, 50% and 75%). The IVs which must be controlled and kept the same are the:

- type and amount of all other ingredients
- mixing method and time
- amount of mixture placed in each cake case or tin
- oven, position in oven, cooking temperature and cooking time
- presentation of the final result (e.g. the samples must all be plain, not iced, the same size, and presented in good light so they can be fairly assessed).

Coding samples

The coding of the samples should also be controlled. Samples should be given a code number or letter so that assessors do not know which one they are trying. This is sometimes called **blind testing**. The coded samples should be presented in random order to prevent the individual assessors from trying all the samples in the same order as each other. For example, the coded samples could be as follows:

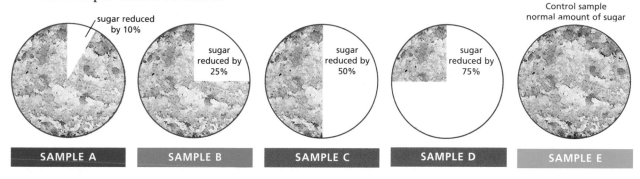

Control sample
normal amount of sugar

sugar reduced by 10%

sugar reduced by 25%

sugar reduced by 50%

sugar reduced by 75%

SAMPLE A   SAMPLE B   SAMPLE C   SAMPLE D   SAMPLE E

and this could be the order of presentation:

SET 1:
SAMPLE D   SAMPLE B   SAMPLE E   SAMPLE A   SAMPLE C

SET 2:
SAMPLE C   SAMPLE B   SAMPLE E   SAMPLE D   SAMPLE A

SET 3:
SAMPLE E   SAMPLE D   SAMPLE B   SAMPLE C   SAMPLE A

To reduce the effect of previous samples on the taste buds assessors should be given water to drink or dry plain crackers to eat in between samples.

It is important to include a **control**, amongst the samples so that the results can be compared against it. In this case it would be a cake mixture with the normal amount of sugar added. If a test like this is carried out, it should be possible to analyse the effects of sugar on the cake mixture.

Sensory analysis tests are described in more detail in Section 6.2.

1 What is an IV? Give examples of five IVs for the following products:
   a) cakes
   b) soups
   c) potato crisps
   d) chocolate biscuits
   e) vegetable curry sauce.

2 What is blind testing?

3 Why are assessors given a drink of water of a plain biscuit to eat between samples?

4 What is a control and why is it needed in a test?

6.2 SENSORY ANALYSIS TESTS (1)

BY THE END OF THIS SECTION, YOU SHOULD BE ABLE TO:

- identify and carry out the main types of sensory analysis tests

Difference tests

The aim of difference tests is to find out if there are any detectable differences between two food product samples.

Are the results significant?

Scientists and mathematicians use statistics (numbers) to show and explain the results of test they have carried out or collections of information they have gathered. They use a formula to work out whether or not a result is significant (important, meaningful).

In sensory analysis tests, a significant result is one which is important enough to mean that the IV that was altered, e.g. reducing the sugar content, has had a notable effect on the sensory qualities of the product.

Paired comparison test

Paired comparison tests help to confirm what a product developer might predict about the effect of altering an IV. For example, reducing the fat content of a biscuit may make the end result more crumbly, drier or harder.

To carry out a paired comparison test, choose a minimum of six people as assessors, and present each assessor with pairs of coded samples. Present the pairs randomly (i.e. AB, BA, BA, AB etc.), then ask questions such as:

- which one do you like best? (called a **preference question**)
- which one is drier/moister? which one is heavier/lighter in texture? (called **specific attribute** questions).

Add up all the As and Bs for each question, then refer to the table opposite to see if the results are significant enough to mean that the IV that was altered (e.g. reducing the sugar content) has had an effect on the sensory qualities of the product.

Triangle test

Triangle tests can be used to show up small differences between products. When the results are not significant, it means that the alteration to an IV has had very little effect on the sensory or eating qualities of the product.

A team of experienced testers taste coded sets of samples and list the differences they detect.

To carry out a triangle test, choose a minimum of five assessors. Present each assessor with coded samples in sets of three, two of which are identical, the other being the odd one out. It is not necessary to tell them in what way one would be different from the other two. Present the samples randomly, e.g. 122, 212, 221, 112, 121, 211. Add up the number of correct answers (i.e. those where the odd one out was correctly guessed) and use the table below to assess your results.

'Two-out-of-five' test

To carry out a two-out-of-five test, choose a minimum of five assessors. Present each assessor with coded sets of five samples (randomly), three of which are the same, and two of which are different from the other three and from each other. The assessors must decide which two are different. If they cannot detect a difference, the assessors must tick a box which says 'no difference'. Add up the number of correct answers, then refer to the table below.

If no significant differences are detected in a 'two-out-of-five' test, it can be assumed that altering an IV has not had a noticeable effect on the eating or sensory qualities of the product.

Number of assessors or tests	Minimum number of votes or correct answers that would be significant in these tests			
	Difference tests		Triangle	Two-out-of-five
	preference question	specific attribute question		
5	–	–	4	3
6	6	6	5	3
7	7	7	5	5
8	8	7	6	3
9	8	0	6	4
10	9	9	7	4
11	10	9	7	4
12	10	10	8	4
13	11	10	8	4
14	12	11	9	4
15	12	12	9	5
16	13	12	9	5
17	13	13	10	5
18	14	13	10	5
19	15	14	11	5
20	15	15	11	5

1 What is the difference between a preference question and a specific attribute question?
Give examples.

2 Why is it important to know if the result of a test is significant or not?

6.2 SENSORY ANALYSIS TESTS (2)

- identify and carry out the main types of sensory analysis tests

Ranking tests

The aim of these tests is to put in order the intensity of a particular characteristic in a food product. Ranking tests are quite often used in market research to ask consumers to say in which order they prefer samples of a food product. To carry out a ranking test, choose a minimum of ten assessors. Present each assessor with a set of coded samples (arranged randomly), then ask them to rank them in order, according to the characteristic you want to test (e.g. least salty to most salty) or a hedonic descriptor (e.g. most liked to least liked) which is called a **hedonic scale** or ranking. Set out the results as in the example below:

Results of ranking tests					
Assessor	Order of samples				Rank sums
	A	B	C	D	
A	2	3	1	4	10
B	2	4	1	3	10
C	3	4	1	2	10
D	1	3	2	4	10
E	2	4	1	3	10
Rank sums	10	18	6	16	50

The results show that B and D are similar, C is different from A, and C is different from B and D.

	1	2	3	4	5
a)	1	2	3	4	5
b)	dislike a lot	dislike a little	neither like nor dislike	like a little	like a lot
c)	much too salty	too salty	just right	too little salt	much too little salt
d)	least sweet				sweetest

Rating tests

In these tests, assessors are asked to rate a particular attribute or preference for a food product on a numbered or worded scale. For example:
The scale can be **unipolar** (goes one way) as in example D, or **bi-polar** (goes from one extreme to another) as in example C.

To carry out a rating test, choose a minimum of 20 assessors, and present each one randomly with a set of coded samples. Ask them to rate them according to a particular scale (this will depend on what you want to find out). Plot the data (the answers that are given) as either a frequency distribution graph, a bar chart or a pie chart.

Profiling tests

This is often called **sensory profiling**, and is used to obtain information about what the differences are between products and how much of each difference there is. For example, a manufacturer might want to compare their own brand of tomato ketchup with three other brands in order to establish why other brands have larger or smaller sales figures, and what improvements could be made to their own brand to increase its sales figures.

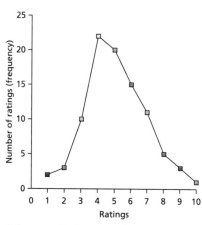

A bar chart

A frequency distribution graph

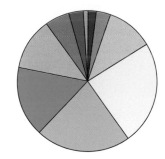

A pie chart

To carry out a profiling test, choose a minimum of six assessors, and present each one randomly with a set of coded samples. Ask each assessor to rate the intensity (on a scale of one to six, where one is least and six is most) of the following sensory descriptors: tomato flavour, acidity, sweetness, thickness and red colour. Add up the answers and work out the mean (average) rating (MR) for each descriptor and brand. Plot them on a spider's plot or star diagram, to provide a visual product profile. A table could be drawn up to show the results.

In the following example, four brands were rated by six assessors. Brand A is the brand leader (it has the highest sales figures). Brand C is the manufacturer's own brand, which comes second out of the four in terms of sales figures.

Brand profiles										
	Tomato Flavour		Acidity		Sweetness		Thickness		Red colour	
	rating	MR	rating	MR	rating	MR	rating	MR	rating	MR
Brand A	6, 5, 6, 4, 6, 5	5.3	2, 2, 3, 3, 2, 3	2.5	3, 4, 3, 3, 4, 4	3.5	5, 6, 6, 5, 6, 5	5.5	6, 5, 6, 6, 6, 5	5.7
Brand B	2, 1, 1, 2, 1, 1	1.3	6, 5, 5, 6, 5, 4	5.2	1, 2, 2, 1, 1, 2	1.5	2, 3, 1, 1, 2, 2	1.8	2, 3, 2, 2, 1, 2	2
Brand C	3, 2, 4, 3, 3, 2	2.8	3, 4, 3, 3, 4, 4	3.5	5, 6, 6, 5, 4, 4	5	4, 3, 3, 4, 4, 3	3.5	4, 4, 5, 3, 4, 4	4
Brand D	3, 3, 3, 3, 4, 2	3	5, 4, 4, 3, 3, 4	3.8	3, 4, 5, 5, 4, 5	4.3	2, 2, 3, 3, 4, 2	2.7	4, 3, 3, 4, 2, 3	3.2

The results show that brand A has a good tomato flavour and red colour, with average sweetness, low acidity and good thickness. Brand B has poor tomato flavour, high acidity, low sweetness, and poor thickness and colour. Brand C has quite low flavour, average acidity, high sweetness, and average thickness and colour. Brand D has average flavour, acidity, thickness and red colour, and above average sweetness.

The results for Brand C indicates that, to improve sales figures, the manufacturer should increase the tomato and reduce the sugar content of their tomato ketchup recipe.

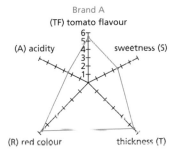

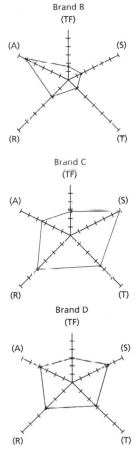

1 What is sensory profiling, and why is it used by food manufacturers?

2 In sensory analysis tests, why is it important to code samples and give them out randomly to assessors?

3 Why is it necessary to have a minimum number of people to carry out a test?

4 Why is it a good idea for a manufacturer to use more than one test to assess a new product?

6.3 TARGET GROUPS (1)

BY THE END OF THIS SECTION, YOU SHOULD BE ABLE TO:

- identify the needs and wants of a range of target groups
- draw conclusions about the suitability of food products for their intended markets

The success of a new product largely depends on there being a group of consumers who need, want and will repeatedly buy the product. These consumers are the **target group** that market research will identify. Market research may also identify a need for which there is no available product. This is called a **gap in the market**, and once identified, manufacturers will be keen to 'fill' it.

Research may find that the target groups have conflicting needs and wants, e.g. they want to eat fresh, 'natural' foods, but need processed convenience foods to fit in with a busy lifestyle. The target group may not be the one which eats the final product, e.g. in the case of baby food, the product has to appeal to both the consumer (the baby), and the provider (the parent) who is the actual purchaser.

Babies

Babies are totally reliant on their parents to provide their food, so baby food product development must take into account the needs and wants of the baby *and* the parent.

Needs and wants

The parent will want to buy food that:

- is wholesome and nutritious
- has an appetizing appearance, smell and flavour (many parents try the food before giving it to the baby!)
- has convenient packaging and is easy to prepare, heat and serve
- contains few if any additives, e.g. colours, preservatives and flavours
- is low in sugar or sugar-free
- has an acceptable price
- is hygienic and safe.

A small pot of yoghurt makes a convenient and nutritious dessert for both baby and parent.

The baby needs:

- essential nutrients for growth and development
- energy-dense, filling food
- food that is easy to eat/swallow, i.e. a safe texture
- hygienic, safe food
- a variety of foods to develop tastes.

Toddlers and young children

Like babies, children in this age group are totally reliant on their parents to provide their food, but start to have more influence on what is bought and prepared for them, by making clear their likes and dislikes. Again, both the needs and wants of the parent and children must be taken into account.

As small children learn to feed themselves they develop an interest in the colour, shape and texture of food.

Needs and wants

The needs and wants are the same as for baby food, but the parent also wants food that is:

☐ easy to hold, use and eat to help develop the child's independence

☐ available in suitably sized portions, especially in restaurants

☐ 'themed' products for parties and other celebrations.

The child now wants interesting shaped, coloured, textured and flavoured foods.

School-aged children

Reliance on the parents is still very important, but the influence of peer groups (people of the same age group), and growing independence put pressure on the parents to buy particular products. Awareness of issues such as environmental pollution, vegetarianism, animal rights, and Third World poverty, start to influence children's thinking and food choice.

Needs and wants

Needs and wants are largely the same as for young children, but parents also want:

☐ convenient products to fit in with out-of-school activities

☐ filling foods to cope with ever-increasing appetites

Many children have a packed lunch every day so there is a large market for items suitable for inclusion in lunch boxes, such as individual wrapped portions of cheese or snack foods and drinks in small packets or cartons.

☐ products which meet current dietary guidelines on healthy eating.

The child wants:

☐ products for packed lunches

☐ environmentally friendly products.

1 Why is it important that a new product meets the needs of the target group of customers for which it was designed and produced?

2 List three needs and three wants for each of the following target groups when considering food products:
   a) babies
   b) parents of babies
   c) toddlers and young children
   d) school-aged children.

3 List some considerations when developing the specification for the following types of food products:
   a) a healthy drink for school-age children, for use in packed lunches
   b) children's novelty birthday cakes to be sold in supermarkets.

6.3 TARGET GROUPS (2)

- identify the needs and wants of a range of target groups
- draw conclusions about the suitability of food products for their intended markets

Ice cream, sweets and snack foods are used by active teenagers to give them an energy boost.

Teenagers

Awareness of world, environmental, religious, political, economic and health issues can be a strong influence on food choice for this age group. There is a gradual transition from parental influence to self-reliance and self-responsibility for providing food. Potential spending power increases. Body and self-image become important, and peer group pressure increases. Body growth is rapid and appetites are often large.

Needs and wants

Teenagers need and want food that is:

- [ ] appetizing, filling and interesting
- [ ] affordable
- [ ] fashionable
- [ ] environmentally friendly
- [ ] quick and easy to prepare
- [ ] suited to a busy and energetic lifestyle
- [ ] easy to eat standing up or 'on the move'
- [ ] not exploiting Third World producers or animals.

Single people

This group includes students, separated/divorced people, widows/widowers and young people in their own accommodation. Many have a busy lifestyle, a small income or limited storage, preparation and cooking facilities at home.

Needs and wants

Single people's needs and wants are largely the same as for teenagers, but they also want:

- [ ] products sold in small packs and suitable portion sizes
- [ ] ready made or partly prepared meals that require little preparation or cooking
- [ ] products which are suitable for entertaining and for special occasions
- [ ] products which are easy to store.

Disabled people

The needs of disabled people vary widely, and are often specific to a particular disability.

Needs and wants

All disabled people need products which are nutritious, affordable and available in suitable package sizes, but in addition they have the following requirements.

Someone who is confined to a wheelchair needs:

- [ ] packaging which is easy to open and reseal
- [ ] products which are easy to pick up and hold while   using
- [ ] adapted shopping trolleys and good customer service from retailers.

People who suffer from arthritis and similar disabilities need:

- [ ] products which are easy to open and reseal, especially jars and bottles
- [ ] products that are easy to prepare and handle
- [ ] products which are easy to unpack or serve out.

Disabled people may have specific needs, such as easy access to shopping facilities, which may limit their choice of where they shop and what they buy.

Visually impaired people need:
- [ ] large print or Braille on labels where possible
- [ ] packaging which is easy to open and reseal
- [ ] containers which are easy to identify by their shape and size
- [ ] a customer service from retailers to help them shop.

Senior citizens

The number of senior citizens is growing every year, and many live on a limited income. The interest in cooking food may often decline when a person is widowed and is just 'cooking for one', and appetites become smaller with increasing age, so food products need to supply a good range of nutrients to help prevent deficiencies.

Needs and wants

Elderly people need:
- [ ] suitable portions and pack sizes
- [ ] a range of 'traditional' products to suit well-established eating habits
- [ ] packaging which is easy to read, open and reseal
- [ ] products which require minimal preparation
- [ ] food that is economical to buy and prepare
- [ ] nutritional meals.

Individual portions and smaller pack sizes are targeted at single people and the elderly, but the relative cost is often higher than for 'family size' packs.

1 List three needs and three wants for each of the following target groups:
   a) teenagers   **b)** single people
   c) disabled people   **d)** senior citizens.

2 Which groups of people are likely to be influenced and affected by the following factors when they buy a food product:
   a) price   **b)** ease of use
   c) status and image   **d)** quality and reliability?
   Give reasons for your answers.

3 List some considerations when developing the specification for the following types of food products:
   a) a range of main meals in individual portions for single people
   b) vegetarian versions of main meals such as casseroles, savoury pies and pasties, shepherd's pie and curry.

6.4 SPECIAL DIETARY NEEDS

There are three main reasons why people might not be able to eat certain types of foods: moral reasons (e.g. vegetarians), religious and cultural reasons (e.g. Muslims) and medical reasons (e.g. diabetics – see Section 6.5).

Vegetarians

There are two main types of vegetarian: **lacto-ovo vegetarians** and **vegans** (strict vegetarians). A person might become a vegetarian because they believe that eating animal flesh is morally wrong, because of religious beliefs or because they consider a vegetarian diet to be more healthy.

Lacto-ovo vegetarians

Lacto-ovo vegetarians will not eat meat or meat products, poultry, fish, lard, suet, fish oils or gelatine, because producing these involves slaughtering the animal or fish. However, they will eat food products from animals, such as eggs, milk, cheese, butter, cream, yoghurt and fromage frais.

Special vegetarian cheese can be purchased. It is made with vegetable rennet rather than animal rennet, which comes from the stomach of a calf.

Suggested foods for a lacto-vegetarian include:

☐ salads with pulses, cheese, eggs, nuts and beans to add protein
☐ savoury vegetable crumbles with nuts and seeds in the topping
☐ vegetable, cheese and nut loaves
☐ burgers or sausages made with ground nuts, breadcrumbs, **tofu** (a soya-based meat substitute), **Quorn** (a commercially made myco-protein meat substitute) or lentils
☐ vegetable curries
☐ pizzas with vegetable toppings, savoury flans and vegetable pies
☐ vegetarian lasagne using lentils, beans, peas and nuts
☐ savoury pancakes with vegetable and cheese sauce
☐ savoury rice with nuts and vegetables
☐ stuffed vegetables.

Vegans

Vegans will not eat any food that is based on animal products. This prohibits them from eating eggs and dairy products, as well as meat and fish. Particular care has to be taken in producing food for vegans to ensure nutritional balance.

There are many varieties of nuts, pulses and cereals which can be used to produce satisfying and interesting meals for vegans. The use of spices, herbs, unusual vegetables and fruits can add variety and flavour.

Suggested meals for vegans include:

☐ bean and vegetable stews (made with vegetable stock)
☐ salads with nuts and cooked pulses
☐ nut roasts with vegetables
☐ soups with cereal (e.g. barley, rice)
☐ vegetable curry and rice
☐ egg-free pasta with vegetable sauces
☐ soya milk used in place of cow's milk
☐ burgers or rissoles made with nuts, beans, rice and breadcrumbs
☐ savoury rice with beans and vegetables.

Extra protein in the form of egg added to the cheese sauce, and beans combined with the vegetables, make a nutritious vegetarian lasagne.

Religious groups

Certain religious or cultural beliefs prohibit the consumption of some kinds of food.

The Jewish faith

Jewish food customs and dietary laws are set out in the Old Testament of the Bible. Foods that fulfil the requirements of the laws are called Kosher foods. Jews who observe these laws may eat only clean birds and meat from cud-chewing, cloven-footed animals, i.e. beef, venison and lamb which have been slaughtered by a Kosher butcher; and only fish with scales and fins. Forbidden foods, which must not be eaten, include shellfish, (crab, lobster), pork, bacon, ham, eels, eggs with bloodspots and gelatine. Milk and meat should not be eaten together, and there should be separate cooking utensils for each of these.

The Islamic faith

Muslims follow the religious teachings of Islam and are not allowed to eat food from pigs. Other meat must be slaughtered by a special ritual, known as Halal. Muslims are not allowed to drink alcohol.

The Hindu faith

Many Hindus are vegetarians, and none are allowed to eat beef because the cow is a sacred creature to them. Milk and milk products are eaten, but strict Hindus do not eat eggs, fish or meat.

The Buddhist faith

Many Buddhists are vegetarian because of their belief in being sympathetic and helpful to all animals.

A Muslim family enjoy a traditional meal together.

1 What are the main reasons why people might not be able to eat particular foods?

2 What are the two main types of vegetarian and how do they differ?

3 From which foods can vegans obtain calcium, fat, vitamin B and protein?

4 Name four foods that Jews are forbidden to eat.

5 What are Halal meats?

6 Find out the names of three Jewish festivals and examples of foods that are eaten at each.

7 Why should lacto-ovo vegetarians limit their intake of dairy products?

8 Why should vegans eat a mixture of plant proteins?

9 Why is calcium-enriched soya milk a useful product for vegan children?

10 Why is it necessary for people from different religious groups to check the ingredient labels on foods such as meat products, yoghurts and desserts?

121

6.5 FOOD INTOLERANCES

- understand that some people cannot eat certain types of food for medical reasons

Some people cannot eat certain types of food without becoming ill. This is known as **food intolerance**. This may be caused by a deficiency in certain substances naturally produced by the body, by an allergy or by the body being unable to absorb certain nutrients.

Cakes, desserts and chocolate are manufactured with artificial sweeteners especially for diabetics.

Diabetes

Glucose is carried in the blood to all body cells to supply them with energy. In order for glucose to enter the cells, a hormone, **insulin**, is required to act as a chemical 'key'.

Insulin is produced by the pancreas. If the pancreas does not make enough insulin, the glucose will stay in the bloodstream. The lack of glucose in the cells means they will have to obtain energy from the body fat stores, which will result in a loss of weight and general weakness. This condition is called **diabetes mellitus** (diabetes for short).

Meals for diabetics should include high-fibre, starchy carbohydrate foods, e.g. wholemeal bread, pasta, jacket potatoes, pulses, brown rice and beans, but less sugar and sweet foods, less high-fat and fried foods, and less salt.

A variety of foods, including biscuits, jams, and chocolates, are produced specially for diabetics. They are made with a sugar alcohol (**sorbitol**) instead of sucrose and glucose. Sorbitol is absorbed slowly and converted to fructose in the liver, which prevents the rapid rise in blood sugar level brought on by eating ordinary sugar.

Some people have an allergy to cow's milk products. Soya milk based substitutes are available.

Food allergies

The body has an immune system to protect it from harmful things such as viruses. Sometimes a person's immune system will react strongly to a particular substance. The person is said to be allergic to the substance, and the substance is called an **allergen**. In foods, the allergen is often a protein.

Allergies to cow's milk, eggs, soya, and mono-sodium glutamate (a flavour enhancer) are fairly common. The symptoms can include eczema, asthma, skin irritation, headache and sickness.

Some allergic reactions may cause changes in behaviour. There is some evidence that certain food colours and preservatives may cause hyperactivity (uncontrollable activity and violent changes of mood) in some young children.

Some allergic reactions can be very serious. For example, certain people have an **anaphylactic reaction** (response of the immune system) to an allergen in peanuts. This means that a tiny quantity of the allergen causes their whole body to react immediately and severely in the following way: blood vessels start to leak, the linings of the bronchial tubes swell, causing difficulty with breathing and the lips and face swell, then their blood pressure drops, and the person will collapse. They must be treated immediately with an injection of adrenaline, otherwise they may die. In severe cases, merely touching the food or breathing in particles of the allergen can cause a reaction.

No matter how tiny an amount, the inclusion of nuts in any way, (e.g. if products are prepared near to others that contain nuts) should be highlighted on the product label and on the retailer's shelves in order to warn vulnerable people. Restaurants and other food outlets should also make such information known to customers.

Coeliac disease

Coeliac disease is caused by sensitivity to the protein **gluten**, which is found in many cereal plants, especially wheat. In sensitive individuals, gluten damages the lining of the intestine (the **mucosa**). Why this happens in some people and not others is not clear. The damage prevents nutrients from being absorbed.

Children become unhappy, lethargic (no energy), and have no appetite. They produce pale and bulky faeces, and the abdomen swells. The rest of the body becomes thin, and the child fails to grow properly. Adults with coeliac disease often have anaemia, weight loss and diarrhoea.

Gluten is found in barley, rye, and oats, as well as wheat, so these must not be eaten in any form.

Gluten free cereal products are available for people who suffer from coeliac disease.

1 What does food intolerance mean?

2 Why does diabetes lead to: a) weight loss
　　　　　　　　　　　　　　 b) lack of energy?

3 Find out what the BDA is and what it recommends that diabetic people should eat.

4 Name two foods to which many people are allergic.

5 Name two common symptoms of food allergies.

6 What are people with coeliac disease sensitive to?

7 Name two foods that coeliacs should avoid eating.

8 Find out what malabsorption means.

9 What is an anaphylactic reaction?

10 Why is it important that food manufacturers clearly indicate if their product contains or has been prepared near nuts?

11 What is insulin and why do some diabetics have to have daily insulin injections?

6.6 WEIGHT WATCHERS

By the end of this section, you should be able to:

- understand that some people require calorie controlled meals
- identify the kinds of foods that are appropriate to the needs of slimmers and weight watchers

The number of people who are overweight or **obese** (excessively overweight) is increasing in wealthy countries, such as the UK and the USA.

Being overweight is unhealthy for several reasons. Excess weight puts a strain on various parts of the body and can lead to conditions such as heart disease, high blood pressure, diabetes, osteoarthritis, varicose veins, breathlessness, and skin and chest infections. It can cause unhappiness and low self-esteem (feeling bad about yourself), and may lead to depression. Excess weight can cause complications during pregnancy and operations.

The main cause of weight gain is eating more food than the body needs, and not taking sufficient exercise to use up the extra energy supplied by the food. The unused excess energy is stored in the body as fat.

Energy from food is measured in **kilocalories (kcal)** or **kilojoules (kJ)**. Protein, fat and carbohydrate all supply the body with energy, but fat supplies more than twice the amount of energy than the same weight of protein and carbohydrate:

Energy from food	
Food type	**Energy value**
1 gram pure carbohydrate	3.75 kcal or 16 kJ
1 gram pure protein	4 kcal or 17 kJ
1 gram pure fat	9 kcal or 38 kJ

Losing weight

The only really safe and effective way to lose weight is to reduce the energy intake from food and increase the amount of exercise to use up the energy stored as fat in the body. Many people try to lose weight, and a great deal of money is spent on products developed by the 'slimming industry' to meet this need.

Food products for this target group are regulated by law, and manufacturers should not make misleading claims about what the product can do for people who are slimming. Such food products must not supply more than 40 kcal (167 kJ) of energy per 100 grams, and the food label must make this clear to consumers.

Low-fat and low-sugar products

Meals for people who are trying to lose weight should include a variety of foods, the main guideline being to reduce the amount of fat and sugar. Many 'slimming' products, have been developed where the fat or sugar content has been reduced to lower the energy value of the product, and appeal to the target group of weight watchers. These include low-fat cheese, margarine-type spreads, yoghurts, biscuits, salad dressings, ice-cream and low or no-sugar drinks and desserts. Food that is naturally low in fat such as fruit, vegetables, white fish, poultry, skimmed milk and cottage cheese are also appropriate for this target group.

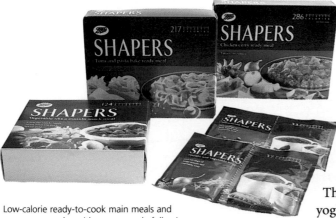

Low-calorie ready-to-cook main meals and soups are popular with many people following a calorie-controlled diet.

High-fibre foods, including bran, wholemeal bread, wholemeal pasta and cereal grains, add bulk to meals to make them more satisfying when the fat content has been reduced.

Cooking for weight watchers

People who are trying to lose weight should use methods of cooking which avoid or reduce the use of fat, e.g. grilling, steaming, boiling and stir-frying, are better than frying or roasting.

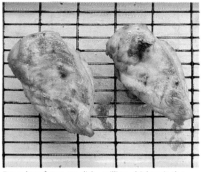

For a low-fat meat dish, grilling chicken is the best choice. Ideally, the skin should not be eaten.

Most food products have nutritional labelling, which shows the energy supplied per 100 grams of the product, and this information can be used to help people keep a record of their daily intake of energy.

Several manufacturers produce complete 'calorie-counted' meals which supply a maximum amount of energy, and make it easy and convenient for people to watch their weight.

Very low-calorie diet regimes

A variety of products are promoted as being able to help someone lose weight quickly and easily. Such products are usually flavoured drinks containing different nutrients, designed to replace two meals a day. The third meal should be a well balanced normal meal. Companies often promote these products through mail order or a person who acts as an agent and visits people in their home. Many people have lost weight through the use of these products, but there are side effects:

☐ weight loss may only be temporary, and once normal eating starts again, weight gain is often very rapid

☐ such products do not encourage a change to healthy eating habits, which is the best way to lose weight and maintain the weight loss

☐ weight loss may result from loss of muscle not fat, which is undesirable

☐ such products are often very expensive.

---

1 What does obesity mean?

2 Why is obesity unhealthy?

3 What is the main cause of obesity?

4 How is energy from food measured?

5 What is the most effective way to lose weight?

6 How are food products for weight watchers regulated by law?

7 How can such food products be designed to be:
   a) interesting   b) low in energy value but satisfying?

8 Why are calorie-counted meals useful to this target group?

6.7 THE FINISHED PRODUCT

BY THE END OF THIS SECTION, YOU SHOULD BE ABLE TO:

- identify the ways in which finished products are presented to consumers
- understand the importance of packaging
- understand the reasons why products are presented in certain ways

Pot noodles only require hot water to be added to make a quick, filling snack.

Preparing fish dishes can be time consuming so frozen ready-to-cook meals with fish are very popular.

Commercially produced food products are presented to consumers in a variety of finished states which may or may not involve a degree of further preparation and cooking.

Ready-to-serve products

Ready-to-serve products require no preparation or cooking. They include snack foods, sliced bread, cakes and pastries, salads (e.g. coleslaw, mixed lettuce), cooked meats, cooked pies, sandwiches and drinks in cartons. They are produced in response to consumer demands for easy to eat, instantly available foods for main meals or snacks.

Ready-to-heat products

Ready-to-heat products (e.g. ready-made meals, popcorn, and soups) and products which require minimum preparation (e.g. 'instant' sauces, soups, snack noodle meals, mashed potato, custard and desserts) are all produced in response to consumer demands for:

- time-saving, easy to prepare meals needing minimum equipment
- hot snack foods which can be eaten anywhere.

Ready-to-cook products

Cake, bread, scone, batter and biscuit mixes, and 'cook-in' sauces for casseroles and curries are all foods that can be purchased ready to prepare and cook. These are manufactured in response to consumer demand for foods that involve them in the preparation and cooking, but without having to collect and weigh out individual ingredients.

Cook-in sauces also enable consumers to have some degree of choice about the finished product by enabling them to vary the ingredients they put with the sauce.

Read-to-cook products include sausages, frozen pies, fish fingers, burgers, oven chips, battered or breadcrumbed fish portions, partially baked bread rolls, frozen vol au vent cases and sausage rolls. These are produced in response to consumer demands for a selection of products to which they can add other items to make a complete meal suitable for a variety of occasions ranging from quick snacks to elaborate pastries.

Presentation for specific target groups

Once manufacturers have researched the needs and wants of a specific target group, they can develop and present products in ways which will appeal to that group. For example, children (and the adults who provide food for them), are a large and profitable target group, and many products are available for different occasions, including:

- packed lunches – e.g. individual portions of cheese, cheese spread, crisps and other snacks, dried fruit, fresh fruit and vegetables, cartons of drinks, confectionery and chocolate bars, small cans of fruit in juice or jelly
- party foods – e.g. character birthday cakes, biscuits, crisps and snacks in various shapes and flavours, cold desserts and ice creams
- 'educational' foods – e.g. number or letter shaped pasta or fried potato products
- every day foods, e.g. cold cooked meat made into a bear's head shape, character shaped pasta products, individual portions of breakfast cereal, cold desserts, fruit juices and drinks.

Packaging and presentation

Technical developments in packaging design have enabled manufacturers to present their products to consumers in a variety of convenient ways.

For example, moulded plastic trays can provide protection for such delicate items as meringues. Cling film and other shrink wrapping can provide an airtight seal (see Section 7.3).

Packaging features	
Feature	**Examples**
ring-pull cans	canned fish, carbonated drinks, pet food
easy-pour cartons	milk, fruit juices
'peel here' lids	cooked meats, cheese slices, yoghurts
individual portions	snack biscuits, crisps, spreads, cereals, cheeses
'pull tab to open'	packets of biscuits, cheese spread triangles
resealable packs	frozen vegetables, rice, bread rolls
squeezable containers	ketchup, cheese spread, sweet sauces and toppings
'tear here' packs	chocolate bars, biscuits, packet mixes for cakes

Disadvantages of packaging

Not all consumers find the new packaging features convenient. For example, those with weakened hands or poor eyesight may have difficulty opening some kinds of packaging. Packaging features also contribute to the cost of a product and to environmental pollution (see Section 7.4).

1 Why has there been an increase in the number of snack food products in recent years?

2 Why has there been an increase in the number of food products that require a minimum amount of preparation and cooking?

3 List five products that are packaged in their own serving dish or container.

4 Why are many products, e.g. breakfast cereals, cheeses and spreads, sold as individual portions, often as a 'pick and mix' selection?

5 What are the disadvantages of products being sold as individual portions?

6.8 CHOICE OF MATERIALS AND COMPONENTS

BY THE END OF THIS SECTION, YOU SHOULD BE ABLE TO:

- identify a variety of reasons why manufacturers use certain materials and components in their products
- give reasons for the use of certain materials and components in specific food products

Acidic fruit such as pineapple is sold in cans with a special lining that will not become corroded by the juice.

For a food product to be successful, it must be suitable for its intended market, and must meet all the requirements of the law concerning health and safety, performance and honesty.

During the development of a food product, the materials (ingredients) and components from which it is to be made must be chosen and assessed carefully. Similarly the choice of packaging must be considered carefully. There are several factors to be taken into account, for example, how the materials and components will:

- □ react with each other
- □ react with the environment inside the packaging
- □ react with the environment once removed from the packaging
- □ alter during transport and storage
- □ alter during preparation and cooking
- □ contribute to the nutrient intake of the consumer
- □ affect the cost of the finished product.

The product development team must also consider current scientific knowledge, consumer awareness and trends concerning:

- □ healthy eating
- □ food intake and long-term health
- □ the use of additives in foods and their effect on long-term health
- □ methods of farming and food production
- □ the use of resources, wastage and pollution
- □ the food requirements of people from different cultural backgrounds
- □ the appreciation of foods from different countries and cultures.

Materials and components		
Material/component	**Food product**	**Requirements and reasons for use**
dried yeast	bread dough mix	must not become inactive too quickly during storage; must not react during storage but must become active once water is added; must be of sufficient strength to raise mixture
batter	frozen battered fish	must be thick enough not to break off fish when fried or baked
fat	chocolate bars for export to hot countries	must melt at higher temperature than those made for UK market without losing the 'mouthfeel' quality of the product
metal for can	canned pineapple in own juice	must be coated inside to prevent acid corrosion
fat	healthy low-fat spread	must be low in saturated and trans-fatty acids; must be high in poly-unsaturated fatty acids
sweetener	sugar-free orange squash	must be from the list of permitted artificial sweeteners e.g. aspartame, acesulfame potassium, saccharin

1 List five factors a food manufacturer needs to consider when choosing materials and components for a new product.

2 What will a food manufacturer need to consider when choosing materials, components and packaging for: a) a puréed vegetable meal for a six-month-old baby b) a frozen vegetarian lasagne meal for one person c) a range of ready meals using recipes from different cultures

6.9 COMPARING BRANDS AND PRODUCTS

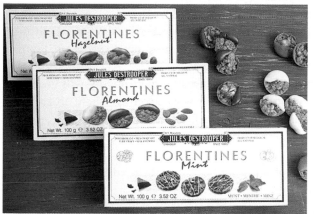

Some manufacturers produce new flavours in an existing successful range in order to benefit from brand loyalty.

An important process in the development of a new food product is for the manufacturer to compare all aspects of the product with similar products made by other companies. The aim is to assess how the new product could be made more attractive to consumers, so that improvements can be made before it is launched onto the market.

The development team will examine the following information when comparing products:

☐ their own market research on consumer reactions to other brands and **brand loyalty** (why consumers repeatedly buy the same brand)

☐ sales figures for other brands (if available)

☐ how long other brands have been on sale – it might be difficult to attract consumers away from a long established product

☐ the target market(s) for other brands – it may be possible to attract an alternative group with the new product

☐ the brand image of other products, e.g. cheap, reliable, healthy, exotic,

☐ cost and effect of advertising in different media

☐ the design of packaging and labelling for the product: is it attractive, convenient and informative for the consumer?

☐ price of the product

☐ product and sensory analysis (see Sections 6.1 and 6.2) to establish what gives one product and brand a higher score than another

☐ the number of uses of the product

☐ storage life and cooking time and method for the product.

As a result of these comparisons, the development team will be able to recommend ways in which the new product could be improved, what its strong points are and how it could be advertised and marketed in the best way to beat the competition.

1 What are 'brand loyalty' and 'brand image'?

2 What makes the following products versatile (able to be used for different occasions):
a) ready-made pasta sauce (tomato, onion and herbs) b) condensed mushroom soup c) plain fromage frais or crème fraîche d) minced Quorn e) canned pineapple rings in natural juice?
Give examples of the different ways in which they could be used.

3 What specific information might a development team look for when comparing the following new products with existing similar ones:
a) a low-fat spread b) an instant cold dessert c) a healthy image savoury snack made from potatoes d) a healthy image ice-cream
e) a range of main meals sold in long life packaging that does not require the product to be refrigerated before opening?

7.1 QUALITY

- understand the meaning of quality
- understand the difference between quality of design and quality of manufacture
- identify ways in which quality control can be achieved in the development of food products

The word **quality** means that a product is of a particular level of excellence or standard. Food manufacturers use a variety of words and phrases to describe the quality of their products, including **condition** (e.g. 'this product should reach you in perfect condition'), **class** (e.g. fruit and vegetables are often labelled as class 1, 2, etc.), **value** (e.g. 'value line' products or 'excellent value for money'), **grade** (e.g. 'conservation grade' cereal products which have been grown using selected fertilizers and pesticides with organic growing methods) and **standard** (the manufacturer aims to maintain a high standard).

For a manufacturer to be successful, and meet legal requirements such as *The Food Safety Act* (see Section 8.5), it must aim to promote, improve and maintain quality in all its products.

For consumers, a product's consistently high quality will give them confidence in the manufacturer, and will encourage them to continue buying that product and to try others from the same range.

Quality of design

The quality of design of a product can be measured by considering the following questions:

Design criteria	Examples
How far does it meets the needs and wants of its target consumer group?	Does a food product for a baby contain any unnecessary additives?
How does the product function in relation to its specification?	Does an instant pudding set quickly, or an instant soup dissolve quickly without lumps? Does it meet its shelf-life specification?
How user-friendly it is it?	Does its packaging open easily? Does it give clear cooking instructions?
How appropriate is its style for its target consumer group?	Animal-shaped oven baked potato shapes are aimed at children.
How versatile is it?	A canned sauce could be used with a variety of meats or vegetables
How suitable are the ingredients, materials and packaging used?	Does the product stay in good condition? Does one particular spice overpower the flavour of the product?
What is its effect on the environment, including the processing of raw materials?	Does this result in waste materials or chemicals? How much energy is used during manufacture and distribution, and final disposal? How much packaging has to be thrown away?

Quality of manufacture

The quality of manufacture can be measured by considering the following questions:

Manufacturing criteria	Examples
How does the product look, taste and smell?	Are biscuits a consistent shape and thickness? Are the flavourings on potato crisps evenly distributed?
How safe is the product?	How well does the packaging prevent spoilage and contamination?
How durable is the product ?	Do cracker biscuits remain undamaged after handling by machinery and people in the distribution chain? Are decorations on mass produced cakes put on neatly?

Quality control

Quality control is the method a manufacturer uses to check that quality is maintained throughout all stages of product development and manufacture. A range of checks can be carried out, such as:

Checks	Examples
How are raw materials grown, produced, harvested, slaughtered, processed and stored	What chemical sprays are used?
What level of stock rotation is there in a storeroom or warehouse?	Are any ingredients out of date?
How well is machinery maintained?	Are loose nuts, bolts, screws prevented from falling into the food product?
Is the correct amount of ingredients used for each batch of product made?	Is the weighing and measuring equipment checked regularly?
Is packaging is correctly assembled and sealed?	Are packages airtight?
What potential hazards are there? (see Section 8.4).	What pests/bacteria might be present?

1 What does the word 'quality' mean and what other words are often used on food products to describe quality?

2 Why is good quality important to:
   a) consumers   b) food manufacturers?

3 Give five ways in which quality of design can be measured.

4 Give two ways in which quality of manufacture can be measured.

5 Why is quality control important?

6 Give three ways in which quality control can be carried out by:
   a) a large food manufacturer   b) a consumer in a domestic situation.

7 Why do many new food products fail to be successful?

8 How does the law help to ensure high levels of quality in the manufacture and sale of food products?

7.2 QUALITY ASSURANCE

BY THE END OF THIS SECTION, YOU SHOULD BE ABLE TO:

- understand the importance of quality assurance to create consumer confidence
- identify ways in which food manufacturers give quality assurance

Quality assurance is the term used to describe the promise or guarantee that the manufacturer makes to the consumer, that its products are of a particular standard, and are safe, reliable, well designed and honestly described.

At every stage of the manufacture of a product, strict quality controls need to be applied to make sure that it does not alter or vary from the standard expected by consumers or the specification laid down by the manufacturer. Quality control is aimed at working out and deciding at what stages controls need to take place, rather than waiting until something goes wrong, and then trying to find out why. Examples of where controls may be applied include:

- when ingredients are weighed and measured
- when ingredients are graded and cleaned
- checking for growth of micro-organisms
- checking the consistency, texture, tenderness, colour, or flavour of products as they are made and cooked

The same system of quality assurances can be applied to the food retail and catering industries who are offering a service to consumers, for example:

Food retail – controls may be applied in:

- stock control, warehouse storage, and display of products
- staff training for knowledge of products and interaction with customers
- staff and customer welfare

Catering – controls may be applied in:

- stock control, purchase of ingredients, and storage
- preparation areas of kitchen
- staff training for hygiene and interaction with customers
- preparation, cooking and serving of food

A catering trainee receiving training from a qualified chef.

132

The Quality Management System (QMS)

Many industries, including the food industry, are using **QMS** to help improve quality, and build up consumer confidence in their products and services. QMS has been developed as a British Standard (number BS 5750) and also as a European Standard (ISO 9000) for Quality Management, both of which set out guidelines and standards for the quality of products and services.

Manufacturers and businesses that meet the requirements of BS 5750 are given an **accreditation certificate**, but they must continue to maintain these requirements or they will lose the certificate.

To qualify for the certificate, a company must set up its QMS by producing a manual showing its policy (its plan of action and what it believes in), and listing all procedures, specifications, work instructions (for all workers) and quality records. It must also keep records of, for example, contracts with customers, purchases from suppliers, maintenance of equipment and controls carried out during manufacture such as HACCP (see Section 8.4). It must also keep a record of complaints and how they have been dealt with.

Another requirement is to show that there is co-ordination between various departments in the company and to provide training and review of workers' performance at all levels in the company. All staff should be involved in this process and should be aware of their responsibilities. The QMS should be regularly assessed and adjusted where required.

As well as using QMS, food manufacturers can promote quality assurance in a variety of ways, including:

- [ ] using high quality ingredients
- [ ] offering a refund, or a refund plus a replacement, if a product is defective or fails to please the consumer
- [ ] following up complaints about a product by investigating the cause and correcting the fault
- [ ] advertising, stating the company's policy regarding quality
- [ ] displaying the company logo or symbol of quality on all products.

▥▥ RICHMAN CATERING

Quality Policy Statement

*I*t is the prime objective of our Company to provide and consistently achieve the highest possible standards of food and service within the policy and financial targets agreed with our clients.

Our quality goal is to continuously achieve those aims in the most cost effective manner.

To help achieve this, we are committed to developing, implementing and maintaining a quality system which complies with the appropriate requirements of BS5750: Part 2.

CERT. No. 1337 — GROUP MANAGING DIRECTOR JANUARY 1992

The Quality Policy Statement displayed by a catering company on their restaurant premises.

---

1 What is quality assurance?

2 Find out and write down some examples of quality assurance given by food manufacturers and retailers. Are they easy to understand? Give reasons for your answer.

3 How can food manufacturers and retailers promote good quality assurance?

4 What is QMS and why do many businesses use it?

7.3 PACKAGING DESIGN

BY THE END OF THIS SECTION, YOU SHOULD BE ABLE TO:

- appreciate the importance of packaging design to product development and commercial success
- identify the various stages that are incorporated into packaging design
- identify various features used in packaging design
- appreciate the environmental implications to be considered by the designer

Many companies employ teams of designers who work on every aspect of product development. Packaging design is a crucial element in this process because packaging represents both the product and the company that makes it. It is a means of communicating the **corporate identity** of a company (what they want people to think about them – their 'image').

The packaging design team needs to communicate and exchange ideas with other teams in the product development process, including:

☐   the market research team
☐   the product engineering team
☐   the component and materials buying team
☐   the quality control team.

The packaging design process

The packaging design team will develop the packaging for a new food product in the following stages.

1   Establish the packaging needs of the product, i.e. size, protection required, amount of information to be displayed, method of opening.
2   Consider the materials which could be used.
3   Consider the type of container to use, e.g. can, bag, carton, tube.
4   Brief suppliers about requirements and inspect their samples.
5   Assess all ideas and discuss them with packaging engineers, printers, marketing department and technologists.
6   Test all ideas for ease of manufacture, protection of food, strength and durability.
7   Assess ideas and decide on the style and presentation of information on the package, e.g. photography, print style, colours, wording.
8   Evaluate and modify packaging designs.
9   Select final packaging and begin manufacture.

The packaging design for one product may have to be adapted to suit a range of different containers in order to maintain the brand image.

Computer graphics are commonly used to assess the impact of a particular design, and modify it before manufacture. Computer graphics can show what the packaged product would look like from different angles and how it would look displayed in a retail outlet. This saves time, cost and resources.

The packaging design team must also take into account how the product will be packaged for transport to and from the factory, warehouse and retail outlet. In this case, the main concern will be the protection of the product, and instructions about stacking, storage and rotation of stock.

Packaging design elements

The company logo

A company might use the same logo on all its products and advertisements to remind consumers of its quality assurance and reliability, and to encourage them to try new products bearing the same logo. A logo may be writing or initials, a picture, a cartoon or a photograph.

Colour

A company may adopt a colour scheme which it uses on the packaging of all its products to remind consumers of the company and to present a specific image to them. Colours are used to attract consumers in various ways, depending upon the nature of the product. For example red is often used for special offer prices. Gold is often used to signify a high quality, expensive or exclusive product.

Pictures

A company may use a painting by a famous artist to promote a product e.g. chocolates or wine, and give it an exclusive or high quality image. Photographs showing the product served as part of a meal (**serving suggestion**) are used to encourage consumers to buy it.

Pictures of toys, baby animals, the alphabet and numbers are often used to signify that a product is for babies and young children.

Ease of opening and use

Customer convenience should be a high priority. Packaging that opens easily without spillage is likely to succeed, especially if the target consumer group is the elderly or the snack market.

High-speed packaging

Modern food processing plants (factories) turn out thousands of products every day. For fast and efficient production packaging must be designed so that machines rather than people can package and wrap products.

Packaging and the environment

The cost of packaging is included in the price consumers pay for a product. Packaging has to be disposed of and is a major concern to people who worry about the effect of waste disposal on the environment (see Section 7.4). Pressure groups are trying to encourage manufacturers to use less packaging, in order to save resources (including oil and trees) and to reduce the amount of pollution caused by waste disposal. Packaging design needs to take account of these concerns and try to use less packaging, recycled materials, materials than can be recycled or biodegradable materials.

The design and operation of all closures and pouring devices on packaging must be well researched and checked.

---

1 Why is good packaging design important for:
   a) consumers   b) food manufacturing companies?

2 Why is market research important in packaging design?

3 Many supermarkets now sell 'value for money' products, which are priced considerably lower than other similar products. How could costs be kept down in the design of the packaging?

4 How could packaging designers meet the needs of:
   a) blind consumers   b) consumers with arthritis
   c) consumers with severe allergies to certain foods?

5 How do pictures and other visual images (e.g. a bottle of low calorie salad dressing with a narrow 'waist') help to promote a product?

By the end of this section, you should be able to:

- appreciate the environmental problems caused by packaging
- identify the responsibilities of manufacturers, local authorities and consumers in limiting such problems
- identify ways in which resources can be recycled

Approximately 70 per cent of household rubbish consists of packaging materials, a large proportion of which comes from food products. This has to be disposed of by the local authority, either in landfill sites, by incineration (burning), or in some cases by recycling.

The increase in snack and fast food consumption outside the home has led to problems of litter in public places which, apart from being unsightly, can lead to problems with vermin such as rats and foxes.

Huge quantities of waste packaging are disposed of in landfill sites.

The manufacture of packaging materials causes a number of environmental problems. The felling of trees to manufacture paper and card causes damage to **ecosystems**. The use of chemicals in the manufacture of plastics causes air, land and water pollution, while mining of land to extract metals causes damage to natural habitats.

More environmental problems are caused after the packaging has been manufactured and used. Many packaging materials, particularly plastics, cannot be recycled and are not **biodegradable** (they do not rot away), and therefore stay in the ground on a landfill site. Landfill sites may also develop problems such as a build-up of methane gas produced by rubbish that does rot. This can present a hazard to local residents. Many materials, particularly plastics, give off toxic fumes when **incinerated** (burned). These fumes must be filtered out to prevent them from contaminating the air.

Local councils provide recycling centres where people can dispose of clean, empty glass and plastic bottles, tins, paper and cardboard that quickly accumulate at home due to food packaging.

Tackling environmental problems

Food manufacturers have often been criticized for using too much unnecessary packaging. Various campaigns and pressure groups have been formed to encourage manufacturers to face up to their responsibilities in protecting the environment. Manufacturers are being asked to minimize their use of packaging and ensure that any paper or card used comes from trees grown in well managed and **sustainable** (replaceable) forests. In many forests felled trees are now replaced, ideally with the types of tree that are naturally found there.

Manufacturers should discontinue using any environmentally undesirable processes such as the bleaching of wood pulp by chlorine, and wherever possible they should use packaging that can be recycled.

Environmentalists have also persuaded many local authorities to operate recycling centres, provide separated household rubbish bins for recycling packaging and help householders to recycle food waste in a compost bin for use in the garden.

Consumers have been encouraged to:
- dispose of packaging thoughtfully
- actively seek to buy products that use minimum packaging
- avoid individually wrapped products
- recycle packaging
- re-use carrier bags
- ask for better recycling facilities from their local authority
- ask the government to support legislation for minimum packaging.

Recycling

Mixed packaging, e.g. containers that have layers of metal foil, plastic and card or paper, is very difficult to separate. Some packaging, however, is easy to separate and recycle, e.g. glass, metal cans, paper. Some plastics can be recycled, but it is not always easy to identify them. Some manufacturers indicate if the packaging can be recycled by printing a symbol on it, but the consumer has the responsibility ensuring that this happens. The manufacturer has no control over the final disposal of its packaging. Both consumers and manufacturers should ensure they have recycling facilities rather than just one large waste container.

This food chain employs contractors to recycle waste polystyrene packaging.

1 Why has there been an increase in household rubbish in recent years?

2 How does packaging manufacture affect the environment?

3 Why are many local authorities looking for alternative ways of rubbish disposal other than landfill and incineration?

4 Why does packaging cause problems in landfill rubbish sites?

5 Examine some packaged food products (e.g. biscuits, cakes, frozen foods, snack foods) and list the parts of the packaging you consider to be essential and those you consider to be unnecessary. Give reasons for your answer.

6 How can consumers show responsibility for the environment when purchasing, using and disposing of packaged food products?

7 How can manufacturers and retailers be encouraged to be more responsible for the environment?

8 How can local authorities be encouraged to be more responsible for the environment?

7.5 PRESENTING A NEW PRODUCT

- identify ways of presenting a new product
- understand the importance of presentation and how it can be made effective

The success of a new product depends a lot on the quality of its **presentation** (how it is introduced) to a target group of consumers. No matter how good a product is, if it has been poorly presented consumers may not be tempted to try it.

The success of the presentation of a product is dependent upon these processes:

☐ the design of the packaging (see Section 7.3)
☐ the communication of a message about the product
☐ the promotion of the product (see Section 7.6).

Packaging design

Consumers' first impressions of a product are usually based upon its packaging. Packaging therefore needs to present an image about the product, in the form of attractive visual messages and special features such as being easy to open.

A product developer needs to convey a clear 'image' to consumers about their product, for example:

☐ healthy, energetic, adds to enjoyment of life
☐ superior, high quality, award-winning
☐ reliable, consistent, trustworthy
☐ trendy, modern, suits your lifestyle
☐ convenient, no-fuss, uncomplicated
☐ thoughtful, caring, environmentally friendly
☐ luxurious, extravagant, for a special occasion.

Cereal manufacturers like to project a 'healthy eating' image with many of their products.

Communicating a message

Messages about new products are communicated by advertising through the media of television, radio, magazines, newspapers, information leaflets and hoardings (large display boards). Research has shown that in order to change people's behaviour and persuade them to buy a new product, the message must be credible (believable). People are more likely to believe and trust someone they know, so many companies use celebrities to advertise their products. Personal recommendation by a friend is also known to be effective in changing behaviour.

Many companies use interviews with people of a similar type to their target group to recommend the product in an advertisement. These people are called often called 'satisfied customers'. Familiar and long-standing brand images, trade-names, and trademarks are also used to add credibility to a new product.

Popular cartoon characters are often used to promote new products aimed at children.

Research also shows that the type of message used will have an effect on consumer behaviour.

- Strong messages, e.g. about health or safety, are known to draw attention to a product.
- Emotional messages, e.g. about children, animals and nostalgia, may promote favourable feelings.
- Humourous messages are good at attracting attention, but should not be used to belittle consumers, or be so funny that only the humour and not the product is remembered.
- Repetitive messages tend to be remembered for a while but are easily forgotten.
- Loud, aggressive, fast-moving, brightly coloured and painful messages tend to result in the product being remembered as the brain tries to get rid of the other unpleasant images in the message.
- Claims about a product are more believable if they are backed up by evidence such as figures comparing the energy value of one product with that of another.
- The method known to produce the most change in consumer behaviour is the use of messages which show both sides of an argument by comparing the new product with other makes.

1 What does presentation of a new product involve?

2 List four types of image that new products can convey to consumers.

3 Why do many companies use well-known people to advertise their new products?

4 What types of message about new products can be communicated to consumers? Give examples of food products which are promoted by each type of message.

7.6 PROMOTING A NEW PRODUCT

- understand the stages involved in promoting a product

Promotion of a new product takes place in stages.

Stage one

Potential consumers are made aware of the launch of a new product in various ways, such as simple advertisements, press releases sent to magazines and information on labels and packaging of existing products.

When a new product is given a nationwide launch it is heavily advertised on posters, in magazines and on television.

Stage two

Next the manufacturer releases more information emphasizing the brand name to promote 'brand awareness'. This could be done by distributing leaflets and free samples to households in a trial area. This is called **trialling**, and is often used to evaluate the potential success of a product before it is offered for sale in other areas.

Stage three

The next step is to promote the product at the point of sale. This might be done by using an eye-catching display with free information about the product such as recipe and meal ideas, nutritional value and manufacture. Some products are displayed on a tasting/sampling stand perhaps with free

Children can be attracted to new products by the toys and novelties offered with them.

samples of the product and give-away toys, pens, hats or badges, all bearing the product name. This may be combined with advertising throughout a shop by poster displays, messages to customers on the public address system, and promotional badges or hats worn by staff. Often a new product will have a special introductory offer price (e.g. three for the price of two, half recommended price, money-off coupon or 50 per cent free).

Other aspects of food promotion

Research has also revealed that people tend to select what they notice, so the product must attract attention. Most people are exposed to between 250 and 2,000 product advertisements a day but pay attention to only a small percentage of these. The presentation therefore must make the product stand out from the others. Presenting a product to particular types of people is more effective than presenting it to the whole population, so the presentation must be aimed at the right target group. People will not buy a product if the message which is presented to them goes against their beliefs or those of the people they mix with. For this reason, market research and evaluation should be thorough to avoid offending people.

When a new food product or an addition to an existing range is launched, shops are supplied with promotional leaflets, signs and posters. Shoppers may be offered free samples to taste or take away.

1 List the ways in which a new product can be launched and promoted.

2 Why must the presentation of a new product:
   a) attract attention
   b) be aimed at the right target group
   c) match the beliefs of a target group?

3 What process will a food manufacturer have to follow to produce, promote and successfully sell an existing product (e.g. a snack food) with a new flavour and appearance?

8.1 RESPONSIBILITY FOR HEALTH AND SAFETY

BY THE END OF THIS SECTION, YOU SHOULD BE ABLE TO:

- identify the responsibilities of designers, producers, retailers and consumers in upholding good health and safety measures

In the food industry there are health and safety hazards at each stage throughout production, retail, preparation and consumption of every product.

Responsibility for ensuring high standards of health and safety at each stage of the production process rests with every worker, who must be given clear instructions and training by their manager concerning the use of machinery and tools, the storage of food products, the control of micro-organisms, the use of dangerous chemicals, first aid and safety procedures. Managers are also responsible for providing their workers with rest rooms and toilet facilities, and must display health and safety notices for both their workers and the public to read and follow.

Strict **legislation** (laws) about health and safety sets out rules which must be followed (see Section 8.5).

Responsibility for health and safety also rests with designers of both machinery and food products, product developers and consumers.

Examples of responsibilities

Producers are responsible for:

- [ ] maintaining, storing and using safe farm machinery
- [ ] limiting the use of chemicals such as pesticides
- [ ] maintaining the health of livestock through practices such as sheep-dipping, veterinary inspection and good feeding
- [ ] providing farm workers with protective clothing
- [ ] cleaning equipment used to collect produce, e.g. milking equipment and storage tanks.

Manufacturers and processors are responsible for:

- [ ] regular inspection and maintenance of machinery
- [ ] using thorough hazard control procedures (see Section 8.4)
- [ ] packaging products with tamper-proof seals to protect consumers
- [ ] providing regular health checks for all employees
- [ ] providing workers with protective clothing to prevent harm to them and contamination of products by them
- [ ] using only ingredients, e.g. additives, that have been approved for use in foods.

Designers have responsibility for:

- [ ] giving clear instructions on packaging for using, opening, storing and cooking a product
- [ ] designing industrial machinery with protective guards
- [ ] designing equipment which is safe to use, e.g. a food processor motor that will only operate when the lid is on, and will stop if the lid vibrates loose
- [ ] incorporating good design features, e.g. pan handles that do not get hot, are easy to grip, and support the weight of the pan and its contents
- [ ] considering all groups of consumer, e.g. left-handed, disabled, partially sighted and children
- [ ] designing safe packaging, e.g. a ring-pull for a drinks can that does not expose sharp edges.

Operators on food production lines wear protective overalls or aprons, a head covering to protect against loose hairs, and gloves so that food is untouched by hand.

Retailers are responsible for:

- correct storage of food products before sale
- strict stock rotation so that the older products are sold before newer ones
- checking for products which are past their use-by date and removing them from sale
- safe stacking of products on shelves
- safe access for customers into and around the shop and clearly visible exits in case of fire
- thorough cleaning of tools and equipment used for cutting and serving.

It is the responsibility of **restaurants** and **canteens** to:

- ensure thorough cooking and heating of foods
- ensure correct storage of foods
- dispose of waste food and rubbish safely
- implement regular health checks for staff
- provide a safe, well lit and ventilated kitchen for staff to work in.

Workers in all parts of the food industry should:

- report to their managers any hazard or risk
- ensure that all health and safety procedures are followed.

Consumers should:

- follow the instructions given by the manufacturer for storing, opening, using, cooking and disposing of a product
- report any cases of food poisoning to their doctor
- rotate stocks of food products in the home to ensure food eaten is as fresh as possible.

To avoid accidents, knives should never be left in sinks.

1 Which groups of people have responsibility to make sure that food products are safe when they are finally served for someone to eat? Give reasons for your answer.

2 Identify the hazards and risks to health in the following situations:
   a) a mobile take-away van selling burgers and hot dogs
   b) a mobile fresh meat or fish van selling produce in an open air market on a hot day in July, in which one of the people serving has a heavy cold
   c) a wedding reception buffet for 150 people, served in a marquee on an August afternoon, and including items such as prawn vol au vents, chicken sandwiches, cream-filled meringues, eggs in mayonnaise (made with fresh egg yolk) and meat pâté
   d) a week's supply of food shopping (including fresh and frozen poultry and meat, ice-cream, cream cakes, milk and frozen fish) left in the boot of a car for one-and-a-half hours (in carrier bags) in June.

8.2 MICRO-ORGANISMS

BY THE END OF THIS SECTION, YOU SHOULD BE ABLE TO:

- understand what micro-organisms are and how they affect food
- understand the need for hygienic practices in the food industry and home

Micro-organisms are **microscopic** (very small) animals and plants, often single-celled. There are three main groups: **yeasts**, **bacteria** and **moulds**. Food can become unfit to eat if it is **contaminated** (infected) with micro-organisms. These can cause food poisoning, which may lead to serious illness and possibly death.

As they are found in the air, in soil, in water, on animals, on humans, in dust, in rubbish, on equipment and in many other places, **micro-organisms** pose a **high risk** to the safety of products in the food industry.

Yeasts

Yeasts are found in the air, in soil and on fruits. They are single-celled and can grow without oxygen (**anaerobically**). They need warmth, moisture and food to grow and reproduce. They do not grow or reproduce (they are dormant) in very cold conditions, but are most active between 25 and 29°C. They are killed above 55°C.

Yeasts break down (**ferment**) sugars to produce alcohol (ethanol) and carbon dioxide gas. Foods such as fruits, jams and fruit yoghurts may be fermented by yeasts and become unfit to eat. However, some yeasts are harmless and are used to make bread, alcoholic drinks and savoury spreads. They are also used in vitamin supplements.

Fresh or dried yeast is used in bread making.

Bacteria

Bacteria are very difficult to detect in food because they are so small (as many as one million can fit onto a pin head). There are may different types, some of which are very harmful (**pathogenic**) to humans.

In the right conditions of moisture, warmth, food supply, and level of oxygen, a single bacteria cell can reproduce by dividing in two in a matter of minutes. Therefore in only 12 hours, one bacteria can multiply and produce at least 16 million others. This is called a colony of bacteria, and may be visible to the naked eye.

If conditions are not right for reproduction, bacteria can form **spores** which will germinate when the right conditions occur again.

Some types of pathogenic bacteria multiply in certain foods and cause food poisoning by:

- producing waste products (toxins) which irritate the intestine and cause sickness and diarrhoea. Some produce toxins which are not destroyed by normal cooking temperatures, e.g. *Staphyloccocus aureus.*
- being present in large numbers and irritating the intestines
- germination of spores which produce exotoxins (very poisonous chemicals) and cause severe illness and even death

Certain bacteria have been responsible for serious outbreaks of food poisoning, which have affected many people, even causing death.

Escherichia Coli 0157 (E.Coli) – this bacteria has been found in the meat of cattle, pigs, and poultry and unpasteurised milk. It normally lives in the intestines. If allowed to multiply in food, E.Coli can cause potentially fatal food poisoning – e.g. in 1996 an outbreak of E.Coli poisoning lead to 20 deaths in Lanarkshire.

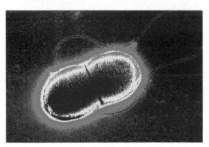

The E. Coli bacteria magnified x 25 000.

Government advice is that meat products, such as beef burgers, must be cooked right through so that there is no pink meat or blood visible. Some pressure groups think that this advice should be very clearly pointed out on food labels.

Listeria monocytogenes – this bacteria has been found in soft cheeses, cook-chill foods, pates and salads. Listeria can grow at low temperatures and may cause still–birth in pregnant women, blood poisoning, pneumonia, and meningitis. Pregnant women, new–born babies, the elderly and sick, and diabetics are particularly at risk and are advised not to eat the products mentioned above. Other bacteria responsible for food poisoning include *Salmonella typhimurium*, *Clostridium botulinum*, *Campylobacter jejuni*, and *Bacillus cereus*.

Food poisoning can be prevented by:
- correct storage of foods
- using different utensils for preparing and serving raw and cooked foods
- through personal hygiene
- protection of foods from sources of contamination such as flies, dirt, drips from thawing foods, pets, bodily secretions
- thorough defrosting and cooking of food
- holding food at a safe temperature before serving
- using food by manufacturer's recommended date.

Moulds

Moulds are minute plants which are only just visible. They need warmth, moisture and food to grow, but can also grow slowly in cold conditions. Moulds reproduce by making spores which travel through the air and land on food. The spores germinate and a new mould grows. Some produce heat-resistant spores which require temperatures higher than 100°C to destroy them, e.g. *Clostridium botulinum*. Moulds produce substances (**mycotoxins**) which travel into the food, and may cause damage to the body if eaten. Some moulds are not harmful and are used in the production of blue-veined cheeses such as Stilton.

Exposure to air causes moulds to grow on cheese, bread and fruit.

1 What does microscopic mean, and why is it important to understand its meaning when handling food?

2 Name two ways in which yeast is used in the food industry.

3 Name five places where bacteria are found.

4 Find out the conditions required for the growth and reproduction of bacteria.

5 How do bacteria cause food poisoning?

6 Why is it not advisable to remove mould growth from Cheddar cheese and eat the cheese underneath?

7 Find out which types of food are a 'high risk' in food hygiene terms.

8.3 THE IMPORTANCE OF HYGIENE

- understand the importance of hygiene rules and practices and the reasons for applying them in the handling of food

The risk of food contamination by micro-organisms can be reduced by ensuring that workers handling food follow a set of hygiene rules.

Weighing and packing salmon steaks in a fish processing plant.

Personal hygiene

- ☐ Wear clean protective clothing when working. Remove the protective clothing when outside the food handling area to keep it clean.
- ☐ Cover all cuts, grazes and skin infections with a clean, waterproof dressing.
- ☐ Tie back or cover hair before starting work.
- ☐ Keep fingernails short. Scrub them clean with a nailbrush before starting work and remove any nail varnish.
- ☐ Remove any jewellery before starting work.
- ☐ Do not handle food if you are suffering from sickness, diarrhoea or a heavy cold.
- ☐ Do not touch your face, hair, ears or shoes while handling food.
- ☐ Do not taste food by dipping your finger into it. If you taste food using a spoon, do not place it back into the food afterwards.
- ☐ Do not smoke, spit, cough or sneeze near food.
- ☐ Always wash hands with a **bactericidal** soap (one that destroys bacteria found on the skin) and hot water after using the toilet; before touching food; after coughing, sneezing or using a handkerchief; after handling cleaning agents or other chemicals; after handling raw meat, fish or poultry; after handling soiled cloths; after handling muddy vegetables.
- ☐ Use a hot air hand-drier or clean paper towel to dry your hands.
- ☐ Avoid touching door handles, walls and handrails after washing your hands.

Food preparation area

- ☐ Keep the preparation area well ventilated, well lit, tidy and regularly and thoroughly cleaned (including the ceiling).
- ☐ Repair any cracks, loose tiles, flaking paint, broken windows etc.
- ☐ Remove all rubbish, waste food and dirt on a regular basis to an area outside and away from the food preparation area.
- ☐ Keep work surfaces tidy. Clean them after each process is completed.
- ☐ Keep equipment clean and covered when not in use.
- ☐ Keep separate areas for preparing different foods. For example, raw meat, poultry and fish should be kept away from cooked foods, while fresh fruit and vegetables should be washed and prepared away from all other foods.
- ☐ Use different chopping boards, bowls and knives for raw and cooked foods.
- ☐ Prevent insect contamination by using fly screens on windows, ultraviolet light insect traps and food covers.

Wiping down chopping boards using a bactericidal spray.

☐ Discourage animal vermin by checking for and removing possible nesting and entrance sites (e.g. holes and cracks in walls, spaces behind cupboards), storing foods carefully, having regular inspections by pest control companies, and preventing an accumulation of rubbish.

Food storage and transport
☐ Label foods to show clearly their date of manufacture and use-by date.
☐ Rotate stocks to use up the oldest first.
☐ Discard any product that is past its use-by date.
☐ Store food at the correct temperature.
☐ Store foods correctly in a refrigerator, e.g. store cooked foods above raw ones, wrap foods such as cheese to prevent moisture loss and the take-up of odours, remove plastic packaging from meat and fish and store in glass or ceramic containers, prevent soil from vegetables from contaminating other foods.
☐ Regularly check the temperature inside refrigerator and freezer cabinets.
☐ Regularly check the temperature of units used to keep cooked food hot.
☐ Protect stored food from contamination by micro-organisms, animals, insects, dust, fumes, moisture or chemicals
☐ Use refrigerated lorries and vans to transport chilled and frozen foods.
☐ Use the shortest possible route to transport perishable foods.
☐ Use protective packaging during transport.
☐ Give clear instructions for stacking and handling products to prevent damage to their packaging or contents.

Cook-chilled products have a limited lifespan. Food manufacturers and retailers must follow strict rules for stock rotation to ensure that food items reach the customer in good condition.

1 Why do micro-organisms pose a high risk to the safety of food products in the food industry?

2 List six rules of personal hygiene, giving a reason for each.

3 Give six rules of hygiene for a food preparation area, giving reasons for each.

4 Why is the rotation of food stocks (including dry goods such as flour) important for food safety?

5 Why is it inadvisable to buy:
   a) dented cans of food
   b) rusted cans of food
   c) a can of food with a 'blown' lid (a raised bulge on the lid that can be pressed down with the thumb)
   d) a can, jar or bottle with a broken safety seal?

6 Why should 'use-by' dates on foods be obeyed?

8.4 THE IMPORTANCE OF SAFETY

BY THE END OF THIS SECTION, YOU SHOULD BE ABLE TO:

- understand the importance of safety procedures and practices for both food industry workers and consumers of their products
- understand the process of risk assessment

Food safety depends on good standards of hygiene (see Section 8.3) applied at all stages of the food production process. Many such rules are enforced by legislation.

Food safety also depends on the industry identifying and controlling risks by regular **risk assessment**. Risk assessment is the process of working out how big a risk is, i.e. how likely it is that someone may be harmed or something may be damaged. One method of doing this is called **Hazard Analysis of Critical Control Points (HACCP)**.

HACCP requires the food manufacturer or producer to look at every stage of production, and identify any **hazards** (mainly the growth of food poisoning bacteria, but also the amount of product in a pack, packaging faults and foreign bodies falling into food).

The point at which a hazard poses a high risk should be noted and reported. These are the **Critical Control Points** and steps should be taken to prevent, remove or reduce the hazard. Once the hazards are under control, they should be closely monitored to make sure that everyone involved in production is carrying out hazard control procedures.

Department of Health
Assured safe catering • Critical control points

	Step	Hazard	Action
1	Purchase	High-risk (ready-to-eat) foods contaminated with food poisoning bacteria or toxins (poisons produced by bacteria).	Buy from reputable supplier only. Specify maximum temperature at delivery.
2	Receipt of food	High-risk (ready-to-eat) foods contaminated with food poisoning bacteria or toxins.	Check it looks, smells and feels right. Check the temperature is right.
3	Storage	Growth of food poisoning bacteria, toxins on high-risk (ready-to-eat) foods. Further contamination.	High-risk foods stored at safe temperatures. Store them wrapped. Label high-risk foods with the correct 'sell by' date. Rotate stock and use by recommended date.
4	Preparation	Contamination of high-risk (ready-to-eat) foods. Growth of food-poisoning bacteria.	Wash your hands before handling food. Limit any exposure to room temperatures during preparation. Prepare with clean equipment, and use this for high-risk (ready-to-eat) food only. Separate cooked foods from raw foods.
5	Cooking	Survival of food-poisoning bacteria.	Cook rolled joints, chicken, and re-formed meat e.g. burgers so that the thickest part reaches at least 75°C. Sear the outside of other, solid meat cuts (e.g. before cooking joints of beef, steaks).
6	Cooling	Growth of any surviving spores or food-poisoning bacteria. Production of poisons by bacteria. Contamination with food-poisoning bacteria.	Cool foods as quickly as possible. Don't leave out at room temperatures to cool, unless the cooling period is short, e.g. place any stews or rice, etc. in shallow trays and cool to chill temperatures quickly.
7	Hot-holding	Growth of food-poisoning bacteria. Production of poisons by bacteria.	Keep food hot, above 63°C.
8	Reheating	Survival of food-poisoning bacteria.	Reheat to above 75°C.
9	Chilled storage	Growth of food-poisoning bacteria.	Keep temperature at right level. Label high-risk ready-to-eat foods with correct date code.
10	Serving	Growth of disease-causing bacteria. Production of poisons by bacterial contamination.	COLD SERVICE FOODS - serve high-risk foods as soon as possible after removing from refrigerated storage to avoid them getting warm. HOT FOODS - serve high-risk foods quickly to avoid them cooling down.

The following HACCPs might require the precautions listed below.

HACCP chicken take-away	
Production stage	**Precautions**
Storage of raw ingredients	Chicken should be correctly chilled; dirty vegetables should be kept away from other food; rice should be stored in pest-resistant containers.
Preparation of chicken and vegetables	Raw meat should be kept away from other foods; vegetables should be washed thoroughly; rice should be inspected for stones and dirt.
Cooking of curry and rice	Ensure that chicken is thoroughly cooked; the curry should be heated to at least 70°C throughout; utensils should be clean.
Serving of product to consumer	Hands should be washed after handling money; food should be at the correct temperature when served; food should be served in suitable containers.
Keeping cooked curry and rice	The temperature of the holding container should be correct; care should be taken with the disposal of unsold products.

HACCP flan production	
Production stage	**Precautions**
Checking freshness of eggs	Eggs should be new laid, and stored in a cool place until required. They should be broken and checked for freshness individually to prevent accidental contamination of a whole batch of mixture with one bad egg.
Storage of raw ingredients	Pastry fats, cheese, and milk, and any meat or fish components should be kept refrigerated, with strict rotation of stock.
Preparation of ingredients	Pastry – mixer should be thoroughly cleaned after batches are made. Filling – equipment such as cheese grating and egg whisking machine should be thoroughly cleaned after each batch. Meat or fish should be prepared in a separate area, and raw meat, e.g. bacon, in a separate area to cooked meat such as ham.
Cooking	New foil cases should be used for each flan. These should be stored away from dust and other contamination. Flans must be thoroughly cooked, to ensure that egg has set and any raw meat is cooked. Flans should be cooled as quickly as possible after cooking and refrigerated until packaged.
Packaging	Packaging should protect product from dust and other contamination, and must withstand refrigeration or freezing temperatures without breaking or disintegrating if moist. Packaging should clearly display heating instructions and use–by date.
Distribution	Flans should be distributed in refrigerated lorries.

1 What does HACCP mean?

2 What are 'critical control points'?

3 What are 'high-risk' foods? Give examples.

4 What are 'low-risk' foods? Give examples.

5 What is 'risk assessment'?

The Food Safety Act 1990

This Act aims to ensure that all food produced for sale is safe to eat, is honestly presented and meets the requirements of the European Union (EU). The Act covers the following areas:

- articles that come into contact with food, e.g. packaging, machinery, storage containers;
- additives, ingredients, drinks, slimming aids, nutrient supplements and water used in the manufacture of food; food sources, i.e. crops, live animals and the farms they come from;
- all operations involved in selling, storing, delivering, labelling, importing and exporting food (including small restaurants, cafés, regular fund-raising events, free gifts and prizes).

Catering premises are regularly inspected.

The Act aims to prevent the sale of food which is harmful to health (e.g. because of not having been heat-treated properly) or which does not meet food safety requirements. This would include food that is mouldy, putrid (rotting), contaminated with a foreign body such as a piece of glass or a mouse, or contaminated with chemicals or antibiotics. It also aims to prevent the sale of food which is not of 'the nature, substance, or quality demanded'. This means that it is not actually what the consumer thinks they are buying, such as a vegetarian sausage that contains meat or coley fish sold as cod. It also refers to false claims and misleading descriptions about food, for example a gâteau might be sold without the decoration shown on the packaging.

The Food Safety Act is enforced by trading standards officers and environmental health officers who are employed by local authorities and councils. Central Government oversees the work of local authorities. The law entitles officers to enter premises (e.g. factories, supermarkets, restaurants, markets or delivery lorries) to investigate a possible offence, inspect food to see if it is safe, take suspect food away to test it and **condemn** it (prevent it from being used or sold) if the conditions found are breaking the law. The officers can also demand improvements to be made to unsatisfactory food premises or even close them down.

Food premises have to be registered with the local authority if they are used on five or more days within five consecutive weeks. Anyone who commits an offence against the Food Safety Act may be taken to court.

As with all legislation, the Food Safety Act is very detailed, so the above information is only an outline.

The Health and Safety at Work Act 1974

This Act aims to protect both employers and employees by increasing awareness of safety, and protect the health and safety of the public who may be affected by the work of a business.

It requires that employers must, as far as reasonably possible, ensure the health and safety of all employees. This includes providing and maintaining safe premises and equipment (including carrying out risk assessments) and giving information, training and supervision on health and safety matters (including first aid, use of fire fighting equipment, fire drill, use of machinery and chemicals and hygiene regulations). Employers are required to write a health and safety policy and allow all employees to read it. The policy should state how the health and safety of employees will be organized, monitored and made effective.

Employees are required to take reasonable care of themselves and any others who may be affected by what they do. They must meet the health and safety requirements laid down by the employer, and must not misuse or interfere with anything provided for the health and safety of others (e.g. a fire extinguisher or a fire exit).

Since this Act came into force, there have been other additions to it covering things such as the control of hazardous substances, risk assessment, design of the workplace, fire precautions, use of computers (VDUs) and using equipment.

This Act is enforced by health and safety inspectors and environmental health officers. They have powers to investigate reports of the law being broken and to remove or prevent the use of anything considered to be an immediate high risk to health and safety. They can order improvements to be made, close down a business or prosecute anyone breaking the law.

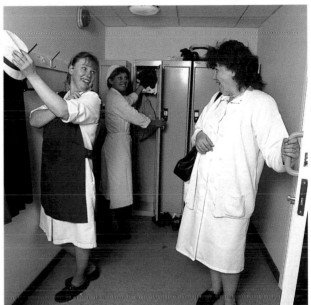

Staff who work in food areas have to wear protective clothing. They must have facilities for changing and lockers for storing their belongings.

1 List three aims of the Food Safety Act

2 What can environmental health officers do if they are told that a food business is breaking the law?

3 List three responsibilities of employers and three responsibilities of employees under the Health and Safety at Work Act.

4 Why are people who run their own catering business required to take and pass a test to get a food hygiene certificate?

5 Find out and write about some recent food poisoning cases which have involved public health inspectors enforcing the Food Safety Act.

6 What specific health and safety training should be given to employees in the following situations:
   a) serving on a delicatessen counter in a supermarket
   b) serving on a fresh fish counter in a supermarket or fish shop
   c) serving in a bakery
   d) preparing foods for a cold buffet
   e) preparing and cooking fish and chips in a take-away shop.

8.6 THE DESIGN OF PREMISES

BY THE END OF THIS SECTION, YOU SHOULD BE ABLE TO:

- understand the need to consider health and safety when designing food preparation areas
- identify the main requirements of the law for the design of food preparation areas

It is difficult to produce safe and hygienic food in a poorly designed and badly maintained preparation area. Hazards such as poor lighting and ventilation, accumulated dirt and rubbish, inadequate washing facilities, and damaged wall, floor and work surfaces pose a risk to both workers and consumers.

The Food Safety (General Food Hygiene) Regulations 1995 set out the main requirements of the law with regard to the design and maintenance of food preparation areas. The regulations are very complex but the main points are that food premises must be kept clean and maintained in good repair and condition, and that the design must meet certain requirements.

The food preparation area

Construction

The layout, design, construction and size of food premises must allow for easy cleaning, must prevent the entry of pests (animal and insect) as far as possible, and must not allow dirt to accumulate.

Maintenance

There should not be any substances that may contaminate food when it comes into contact with them (e.g. lead water piping), and surfaces should not shed particles (e.g. flaky paint, fibres from ceiling tiles).

Condensation, which may lead to mould growth, should not be allowed to build up. This could be avoided by the area being ventilated. It should also be temperature controlled (ideally below 25°C). Food storage areas should also be temperature controlled.

Separate work areas

The layout of the room must allow high risk foods (e.g. raw and cooked meats, fish) to be prepared in a separate area to low risk foods, and avoid the need to carry refuse through food rooms.

With stainless steel and tiled surfaces it is easy to maintain the high standard of hygiene required in food manufacturing and catering premises.

Many modern domestic kitchen have fitted units and appliances that are easier to keep clean than free-standing furniture.

Sinks and washing areas

There should be plenty of sinks, drainers and hot water in the food preparation and washing up areas, with good drainage to remove used water, and plenty of inspection points in case of blockages.

Lighting

The area must have adequate natural or electric lighting (minimum 150 lux in storage rooms to 500 lux in food preparation areas) and must have safe flooring and easy access for staff.

Staff toilets

Good washing, personal hygiene and changing facilities should be provided for staff, well away from the food storage and preparation areas (and separate from customer facilities in restaurants).

---

1 List five hygiene and safety requirements for food premises.

2 Why are the following hazardous to employees and customers:
   a) poor lighting in a food preparation area
   b) cramped working and storage space
   c) old and poorly maintained electrical wiring
   d) inadequate washing facilities
   e) infrequent cleaning of walls, window sills and floor areas behind furniture and equipment?

3 Here is an extract from a (fictitious) report made by local environmental health officers concerning a small independent supermarket.

The shop failed to meet required standards for the following reasons:

1 Boxes of food are stored in a back room on the floor, near to a back door which leads to a yard cluttered with rubbish in boxes and sacks.
2 Boxes of food with use-by dates older than those currently on display in the shop were observed in the store room.
3 The store room is festooned with spider webs and old, well-covered fly papers.
4 Cooked meats and salads are on display on a counter which is not covered by a glass screen.
5 Cooked meats are sliced on a machine that has large amounts of accumulated meat scraps on the blade and on the surrounding worktop.
6 The slicing machine has a loose guard.
7 There is no fire extinguisher on the premises.
8 There is no separate sink for washing equipment used on the cooked meat counter. There is only one sink in the store room which is used for washing hands and equipment.

What repairs, alterations and improvements would the owner have to make, to satisfy the requirements of food safety regulations?

8.7 FOOD PRODUCT LABELLING

BY THE END OF THIS SECTION, YOU SHOULD BE ABLE TO:

- identify the types of information given on food labels
- understand how legislation on labelling protects consumers

Legislation controls what may and may not appear on labels, so that consumers are given accurate information to enable them to choose what to buy.

Food labels must show:

☐ the name under which the product is sold, and any special treatment or processing it has had, e.g. part-baked, smoked, dried, vacuum-packed or frozen.

☐ a list of the ingredients in the product, in descending order of weight (i.e. largest first), including most additives stating either the number or name, including what type of additive it is, e.g. colouring

☐ the net quantity (i.e. the actual weight or volume of the product itself) must be shown somewhere on the label

☐ the date of minimum durability (i.e. how long the product will be in best condition or safe to eat if kept according to the manufacturer's instructions). This is shown as a 'best before' date. Very perishable foods are given a use-by date.

Other requirements are advice on storage, instructions for use of the product, place of origin and the business name and address of the manufacturer, producer, packager or retailer. Sometimes a batch number is also given so that the product can be traced if it causes any problem.

Many product labels also include information (sometimes in the form of a symbol) to indicate that they are suitable (or unsuitable) for a particular group of consumers. The information might convey that foods in the packet are:

☐ suitable for vegetarians

☐ gluten-free

☐ contains nuts

☐ contain no cow's milk products.

Information printed on food packaging must describe the contents accurately.

Nutritional information

At present labelling about nutrition is voluntary, and food companies are only required by law to give nutritional information if they make a claim about their product on the label, e.g. low in fat.

If a food company decides to show nutritional information on a product label, it must follow the EU regulations about *how* such information should be shown on a label. The label must show the energy value in kilojoules (kJ) and kilocalories (kcal) and the amount of protein, fat and carbohydrate in grams (g). When they are included in a food product, the label must also show the amount of saturated fats, sugars, fibre (NSP) and sodium in grams (g) (see Section 4.5).

All nutritional information must be shown as the average amount present in 100 g or 100 ml of the product. It can also be shown per serving, but this is not required by law unless the size of the product is less than 100 g or 100 ml.

Vitamins and minerals must be shown as a percentage of the **RNI** (reference nutrient intake) in the product or **RDA** (recommended daily allowance). RNI is the amount of a nutrient required to meet the daily needs of 97% of each group of people in the population, including babies and children, pregnant women, teenagers and senior citizens. Vitamins and minerals can only be shown if they are listed in the EU regulations, and if the product contains a significant amount of them (at least 15 per cent of the RNI) in 100 g or 100 ml.

FULL CREAM SWEETENED CONDENSED MILK

NUTRITIONAL INFORMATION	
Typical values	per 100g
Energy	1400kJ/330kcal
Protein	8.3g
Carbohydrates	54.3g
of which:sugars	54.3g
Fat	9.1g
of which saturates	5.8g
Fibre	Nil
Sodium	0.1g

VITALITE LOW FAT SPREAD

NUTRITION	100g Provides
ENERGY	639kcal/2629kJ
CARBOHYDRATE	1.2g
of which sugars	1.2g
FAT	70.0g
of which saturates	15.0g
of which monounsaturates	17.0g
of which polyunsaturates	34.0g
of which trans	0.7g
of which cholesterol	nil
FIBRE	nil
SODIUM	0.8g
VITAMIN E	20mg (200% RDA)

Mississippi Mudpie

NUTRITION INFORMATION		
TYPICAL VALUES (MADE UP AS PER INSTRUCTIONS) WITH SEMI-SKIMMED MILK		
	PER 100g (3.5OZ)	PER SERVING (1/8 PACK)
ENERGY	1350 k J	1000 k J
	325K cal	240 k cal
PROTEIN	4.2g	3.1g
CARBOHYDRATES	33.5g	24.5g
of which SUGARS	22.5g	17.0g
STARCH	9.6g	7.1g
FAT	19.0g	14.0g
of which SATURATES	13.0g	9.5g
MONO-UNSATURATES	4.4g	3.2g
POLYUNSATURATES	0.9g	0.7g
FIBRE	0.8g	0.6g
SODIUM	0.2g	0.2g
PER SERVING (1/8 PACK)	240 CALORIES	14.0g FAT

Spicy Refried Beans

NUTRITION INFORMATION		
TYPICAL VALUES	PER 100G (3.5OZ)	PER 1/2 CAN
	289kJ	326
ENERGY	68k cal	77k cal
PROTEIN	4.2g	4.7g
CARBOHYDRATE	11.4g	10.1g
of which SUGARS	0.8g	0.9g
STARCH	11.1g	12.5g
FAT	0.4g	0.5g
of which SATURATES	0.1g	0.1g
SODIUM	0.3g	0.0g
PER 1/2 CAN	77 CALORIES	0.9g FAT

EU regulations state how nutritional information should be listed on food labels.

1 List five reasons why foods are labelled.

2 What must food labels show by law?

3 Why is good presentation of a food label important?

4 Find out how some supermarkets and manufacturers try to help consumers understand the nutritional information given about their products.

5 Why is it important that packaging designers consider carefully how and where information will appear on the products they are intending to promote?

6 How does the law protect consumers with regard to the nutritional information that appears on labels?

7 Why do many food manufacturers use colour codes or symbols on the labels of products to give information to consumers? Give some examples with your answer.

Glossary

additives: substances added to foods for a specific purpose, e.g. to flavour, colour, preserve

aeration: to incorporate air into a product in the form of bubbles

attitudinal descriptors: words to describe what people feel about a product

breaking even: when the sale of a new product makes enough money to cover the cost of its development and manufacture

computer aided manufacture (CAM): the use of a computer to control and integrate all the processes involved in product manufacture

caramelization: the process of changing the colour of sucrose from white to brown by heat

coagulation: a permanent change to the chemical structure of protein brought about by heat, mechanical action, acids or alcohol

component: an integral part of a manufactured product

computer model: the use of a computer to help plan, display, test and modify the design of a product

consumer: a person who buys or uses products and services

criteria (singular – **criterion**)**:** the standards and limits judged to be right for a product

cryogenic freezing: a method of freezing food rapidly, with minimum damage to its structure, by immersion in liquid nitrogen

descriptor: a word that describes a characteristic of a product

difference tests: a method of finding out if there are any detectable differences between product samples

ecosystem: a group of plants and animals interacting with each other in a particular ecological unit

emulsification: the process used to prevent a mixture of liquids, e.g. oil and water, from separating

ergonomics: the study of how easily and efficiently a product performs when in use

evaluation: the assessment of the performance of a product against its original specification

extraction: to remove or separate a substance from others, e.g. by suction, pressure, sieving, or dissolving

feedback: the return of information or part of the output of a system to its source to enable modifications to take place

fermentation: chemical changes to a food brought about by micro-organisms, e.g. the action of yeast on a sugar to produce alcohol and carbon dioxide gas

fortification: the addition of nutrients to a food product to increase its food value

hedonic descriptor: words that describe likes and dislikes about a product

high risk foods: food which provides perfect conditions for the growth and reproduction of micro-organisms which quickly contaminate the food and make it unsafe to eat.

homogenise: to produce a substance which is of uniform consistency

hormones: substances produced by plants or animals which stimulate a process to take place e.g. growth

hydrogenation: the process of adding hydrogen gas to a substance, e.g. vegetable oil during margarine manufacture

input: everything that goes into a system including raw materials, energy, human labour

legislation: laws made and enforced to protect consumers

lifestyle: a person's way of life including what they eat, wear, like and dislike

logo: a printed symbol or trademark used by a company as its emblem

market research: the study of consumers' needs, preferences and lifestyles

milling: the grinding or crushing of a solid substance into a powder or pulp

modify: to make partial changes to a product to improve it or alter a characteristic

nutrients: substances in foods which nourish a living plant or animal by giving it energy, making it grow, help it resist infection and heal

osmosis: the movement of water from a weak solution to a stronger one through a semi-permeable membrane

output: a finished product, plus wastage and by-products that can be recycled

overheads: all the items a business must pay for before it makes a profit, including materials, workforce, accommodation, transport and energy

oxidation: the process in which a substance reacts with oxygen and becomes combined with it

pathogenic micro-organisms: micro-organisms which cause food poisoning and illness

pasteurization: heat treatment of milk and other products to destroy pathogenic micro-organisms, named after Louis Pasteur

pH: a scale used to measure the strength of an acid or alkali

photosynthesis: the process by which green plants use energy from sunlight to convert carbon dioxide and water into carbohydrate

preservation: the process of preventing products from decay so that they can be stored in a safe condition for future use

processing: a series of actions and operations used when manufacturing a product

production schedule: a logical and ordered plan for the production of a product from start to finish

profiling test: a method of assessing the amount and type of differences between different products

quality: a measure of the level of excellence or standard of a product

quality assurance: a promise or guarantee by retailers and manufacturers that their services and products are of a particular standard and are safe, well designed, reliable, and honestly described

quality control: a method of ensuring that quality is maintained throughout all stages of product development and manufacture

ranking tests: a method of putting in order the intensity of particular characteristic of a product

rating tests: a method of rating a particular attribute or preference for a product on a worded or numbered scale

raw material: a material or product which is processed to make another product

refining: the process of removing impurities or defects from a product

resources: all the time, money, equipment, materials and labour which go into a production system

sensory analysis: a method of measuring and assessing the flavour, texture, appearance, smell, and sound of food

specification: a detailed description of how something should be made and what it should contain

sterilization: heat treatment which destroys all micro-organisms in a product

system: a set of operations or items which are connected together to work as a whole for a specific purpose

systems analysis: analysis of an operation to decide how a computer could be used to operate and control it

target group: a group of consumers that manufacturers hope will want, need and repeatedly buy a product

UHT (Ultra Heat Treatment): high temperature, short time heat-treatment, followed by rapid cooling and sealing into airtight containers to preserve foods such as milk, fruit juices, and soups.

variable: a factor or characteristic of a product that can be altered

Index

Acknowledgements

The publisher would like to thank the following for their kind permission to reproduce the following photographs:

p 7 Sainsbury's, p 11 A Blake/Rosenfield, p 16 A Blake/G Buntrock,
p 18 A Blake/Rosenfield, p 20 Telegraph Colour Library (top), Science Photo Library (bottom), p 22 Telegraph Colour Library, p 26, 27 A Blake/Rosenfield, p 28 R J Herbert (top), A Blake/Rosenfield (bottom), p 29 A Blake/Rosenfield, p 30 Holt Studios/N Cattlin (bottom), Telegraph Colour Library (top), p 31 R J Herbert (bottom),
Holt Studios/I Spence (top), p 32 A Blake/J Sims, p 33 Holt Studios/N Cattlin (top), p 34 Holt Studios/R Anthony, p 35 Allied Mills, p 36 National Dairy Council/C Pearsall, p 38 Telegraph Colour Library (bottom), p 39 Kemin Organisation (top), Egg Information Service (bottom), p 40 Telegraph Colour Library, p 41 Still Pictures/T Raupach,
p 46 A Blake, p 47 A Blake/MMB, p 48 Telegraph Colour Library, p 50 A Blake (left), p 51 Cadbury's, pp 52, 53, 54, 55 (top), 56 (bottom), 60, 62 (top) A Blake, p 70 Telegraph Colour Library (top), p 74 A Blake (bottom), p 78 Birds Eye (top),
p 80 A Blake/Rosenfield, p 84 A Blake (bottom), p 85 Samuel Staniforth, p 86 A Blake (bottom), p 90 (top) J Piper, (left & bottom) A Blake, p 93 A Blake, p 95 J Allan Cash, pp 96, 97 S & R Greenhill, p 98 A Blake/C Stebbings, p 100 Cadbury's (top), Northern Foods (bottom), p 103 J Piper, p 104 A Blake/Rosenfield, p 107 M Bennewith, p 109 A Blake, p 112 R Harding/A Woolfitt, p 116 S & R Greenhill (top), Telegraph Colour Library (bottom), pp 117, 118, 119, 121, 132 S & R Greenhill, p 136 Colorific (top), J Allan Cash (bottom), p 137 Still Pictures, p 144 Oxford Scientific Films (centre left), p 146 A Blake (top).

Additional photography by Jacquie Hurst, Norman McBeath and Martin Sookias.

Special thanks to Maria Bennewith, Cilla Piper, Jonathan Smith Crisps, Sainsbury's, Richard Saunders and Sutcliffe Catering.

Illustrations by Paul Bale (Visual Image), Sue Lund, Pentacor plc and Steve Rigby